THE STING...

NEW WRITERS · NEW WRITING

Issue 41 Volume Two | Winter 2019-20

'... God has specially appointed me to this city, so as though it were a large thoroughbred horse which because of its great size is inclined to be lazy and needs the stimulation of some stinging fly...'

—Plato, *The Last Days of Socrates*

The Stinging Fly
new writers, new writing
PO Box 6016, Dublin 1
info@stingingfly.org

Editor: Danny Denton

Publisher
Declan Meade

Poetry Editor
Cal Doyle

Non-fiction Editor
Ian Maleney

Assistant Editor
Sara O'Rourke

Eagarthóir Filíochta
Aifric MacAodha

Design & Layout
Fergal Condon

Publishing Intern
Isabel Adler

Contributing Editors
Dan Bolger, Mia Gallagher, Lisa McInerney, Thomas Morris and Sally Rooney

Printed by Walsh Colour Print, County Kerry

ISBN 978-1-906539-82-5   ISSN 1393-5690

The Stinging Fly gratefully acknowledges the support of The Arts Council/
An Chomhairle Ealaíon.

NEW FICTION

FEATURED POET

CORRESPONDENCES

NEW POEMS

COMHCHEALG

The Stinging Fly was established in 1997 to publish and promote
the best new Irish and international writing.

Published twice a year, we welcome submissions on a regular basis.

The next general open submission window is from
December 2nd 2019 to January 16th 2020.

Our Winter 2020-21 issue will be a special issue celebrating Galway's
designation as a 2020 European Capital of Culture. The editors for this issue are
Lisa McInerney and Elaine Feeney. Submissions are open until November 28th 2019
and again from Monday February 17th to Monday March 2nd 2020.

Online submissions only. Please read the submission guidelines on our website.

Keep in touch: sign up to our email newsletter, become a fan on Facebook, or follow us on Twitter
for regular updates about our publications, podcasts, workshops and events.

stingingfly.org | facebook.com/StingingFly | @stingingfly

Editorial

'This is ridiculous.'
'What is not?'

This simple exchange occurs between two villagers early in Oisín Fagan's novel, *Nobber*, and for some reason it resonated with me far beyond the moment of its saying. It seems to me a summation, or neat responsorial psalm for the times in which we find ourselves living. Brexit is ridiculous (what is not?); borders are ridiculous (what is not?); more than 10,000 homeless in a wealthy country full of empty properties is ridiculous; 'Direct Provision' is ridiculous; the world burning around us while we consume it is ridiculous. What is not?

I speak only for myself when I say this—and when I say that I feel increasingly disorientated in an increasingly ridiculous world, where truth is increasingly obscured, clarity obliterated. I feel disorientated by news coverage, and by the weather, where seasons seem to occur over a week now and not a year, flora budding all winter… And time moves in strange, awkward shifts now, doesn't it? It's as if 'history' has caught up with us. Temporally I mean. Because the internet has rendered us a collective living record log, history is now yesterday. Information travels so fast that there's no lag to allow for retrospection. History is, in fact, this morning.

So truth is a muddle, time is a muddle, and my / our sense of space is pretty askew as well. It seems to me that we live in economies now, not countries. And we spend more and more of our time in virtual spaces and 'non-places' (see Marc Augé: airports, commutes, shopping centres…). Who we are and where we are and what we are is just all increasingly vague to me. And I say this as a privileged white settled Irish citizen. Can you even imagine the disorientation of, say, an asylum-seeker who has fled one place only to be banished to a direct provision centre in another, not allowed to cook for themselves or to work, having to re-tell their story (their *truth*) so many times that it doesn't make sense even to them? Or the disorientation of someone from the Travelling Community, pushed to the geographical, social, educational and legal fringes of society wherever they land in their own 'country'?

I only learned the word 'hauntology' about seven weeks ago, but I increasingly find myself muttering it, returning to it, treating it as some kind of answer. Derrida proffered it as a form of ontological disjunction, perhaps a result of new technologies messing with perceptions of time and space. Three or five decades later Mark Fisher listened to the music of Burial and thought of it as hauntological, visions of lost futures in the present. Tube commuters with shopping bags as ghosts. And so—yes—ghosts as a metaphor, as a symbol of disorientation, haunting as a new, half-dead form of living… Yes? I'm not saying anything new or clever here, but trying to put a finger on and hold down some explanation of this sense of disorientation, this resonance of everything being ridiculous.

Disorientation is, to be clear, the condition of having lost one's sense of direction. Or a state of mental confusion with regard to time, place or identity. It can be a delusion too. The work in this issue, I think, speaks to disorientation. Each piece of work is, in its own particular way, a haunting. Ghosts are entities that haunt because they haven't yet found a way of moving on to what's next. Ghosts haunt because they are disoriented. In various ways and forms, the texts herein try to locate themselves, or their terms, or find themselves lost and confused. Resolution is a hard-fought thing.

Perhaps both writing and reading, as acts in and of themselves, are attempted resolutions to a permanent, low-level state of disorientation? The reader wants to locate some aspect of themselves or their experience in the text, in the world via the text. The writer likewise, except that the writer is behind the wheel. So would that mean then that disorientation is general? Is the author trying to represent or resolve this state? And whatever about the author's role, what is the editor's role? To clarify or sharpen confusion? To collectively obfuscate or to finetune the questions? Is it that the text of the riddle can be the riddle's answer? Who, anywhere, is sovereign in such a world? Are reading and writing rebellious acts against notions of sovereignty? And if disorientation is general, and therefore certain, what can be said to be true? What can be known to have value? Perhaps it is simply the *feeling* that is true and valuable.

This editorial is getting ridiculous. (What is not?)

One of the lines in these pages reads: 'I got here (as if I could tell what *here* is).' Perhaps that's what we can rest on for now: that we got here. Whatever here is.

Danny Denton
November 2019

The Chair

Cathy Sweeney

We take it in turns now.

First, I sit in the chair and my husband administers the shocks, and then, a week or so later, I administer the shocks and my husband sits in the chair. Other couples have their own way of doing things, but this is what suits us.

When it is my turn to sit in the chair, I am almost relieved. In the days leading up to it I become irritable, angry, even on occasion experiencing violent ideations. Often, during this period, I think of leaving my husband, of breaking everything. But when the time comes to sit in the chair I do so without protestation. A sensation of release and expanse overtakes me, as though I am swimming effortlessly in a vast blue ocean, obeying laws of nature that are larger than me, larger than the universe.

It is a different story when it is my turn to administer the shocks to my husband. In the days leading up to that, I am filled with intense feelings of tenderness for him. Or not so much for him as for the idea of husband. He becomes alive to me in a way that usually only happens when a person has died. Often, during this period, I find myself kissing my husband's forehead and the tips of his fingers and, when I leave the house, wearing a vest of his under my clothes. But when the time comes to administer the shocks a red-hot fire erupts in me, flowing through me like lava and annihilating any feelings of tenderness. Afterwards I am calm; even, dare I say it, content.

In between times my husband and I do all the usual things—divide the chores, go to work, come home from work, divide the childcare, go to see a movie, order pizza on Friday nights, plan holidays, talk about finance and going to the gym more often. Time running always that bit faster than we would like.

But our marriage wasn't always so easy.

In the early years, it was mostly me sitting in the chair and my husband administering the shocks, and then, after the babies were born, it was mostly my husband in the chair and me administering the shocks. It takes time to establish a pattern that works for both people in a relationship.

I have heard of couples abandoning the chair completely. It's all the rage in some circles. Live and let live, I say, but I cannot imagine a marriage working without the chair. I mean, where would the anger go? How would you both remember, week to week, day to day, what love is?

Whenever things reach a low point—perhaps my husband has forgotten to do the dishes or I have been fantasising about having sex with a colleague—I think about one time, a few years ago, when my husband was in the chair. I had just administered the last shock and was about to untie the restraints, when I noticed the thinnest trickle of blood coming from his ear. Things like that aren't meant to happen of course, but nothing is perfect, not even the chair. With my finger I traced the thin line of blood from ear to jawline and then, absently, put my finger in my mouth and tasted all the beauty and pain of the world that has ever existed, from beginning to end, in one burst of metallic cherries. You don't forget a thing like that.

The Crab House

Chetna Maroo

I had heard the actors were coming and I felt there was a slight chance of my joining them. In the first week of December, I saw their poster on the wall outside Mrs Wyndham's shop: they were coming, and this time I would be ready. The school term was over. The temperature was minus five degrees and the pavement on Mrs Wyndham's side of the road was covered in ice and grit. There was no one around. I looked up the street, removed my gloves. I took my time. With one hand on the poster, I prised the edges loose with my fingers, making sure the paper didn't slip or detach from the wall too early.

When my mother asked me where I got the poster, I told her I found it lying on the path outside the theatre. I waited to see what she would say about that. She wetted an end of thread, adjusted the lamp on the kitchen table, and kept on with her sewing. I drank my milk. I thought she might say something, but she was going through one of her quiet periods.

I put my empty glass in the sink and went across the hall to borrow a ladder from Mr Levy next door. My mother was the only person in Marlborough who wasn't white, and as usual Mr Levy asked me how come I didn't look like her. I wandered around his place, closing his windows for him so he wouldn't catch a cold in the night. I told him, as I told him most days, that I didn't know but if I had to guess I'd say it had something to do with my father. Mr Levy was unsure how to take that until he saw I was joking with him, and then he smiled. He offered me a shortbread and I accepted it. I knew that if I hung around he would ask me the same thing again in a few minutes before offering me something else to eat. I liked Mr Levy. He was forgetful due to his illness but he didn't dwell on things, and he was good-natured and unstinting in his hospitality. We talked a while, ate biscuits from a plate. When I saw he looked tired, I wished him goodnight. It was true, what I had said to him. I didn't know much about my father, only that he had brought my mother to Marlborough from her family home in India before I was born. It upset my mother to talk about him and she said, at first, that I wasn't old enough to understand. And later, when I was old enough, I told myself I didn't need to know. I just didn't want to watch my mother getting sick from remembering, because there was a depression that could come over her, one that was worst in the winter. Sometimes it would become difficult for her to get up out of bed, and when she did get up, she might have a sudden energy for something domestic, or she might stand in our doorway, eyes shining, telling me to get my shoes on because we were going out, or else she might just stare at the black of our window. You couldn't know beforehand how she would be.

I dragged Mr Levy's ladder across the hall and into our place, where my mother was moving about the kitchen, wiping the worktop and the table. Positioning the ladder by the bed, I climbed up, stepping over the two loose rungs. My mother paused in her work to pull the free end of her sari tight over her bosom and pin it to her blouse, out of the way. As she fixed the pin, a length of dark hair came undone from her braid. It fell over her cheek. I looked at her, thinking that maybe I should tell her I would soon be gone with the actors, but she continued wiping and so I leaned into the top of the ladder and fixed my poster to the ceiling above our bed.

We lived in one room of a brick house at the far end of the town. The roof above our room leaked when it rained and the sewerage was poor. Every now and then, my mother had me go over the damp spots on the walls and ceiling with a clean whitish paint. We lit candles to cover the smell from the sink. Once, a long time ago, my mother bought metres of dark blue polyester and gold-coloured rope, and we made curtains. With the curtains drawn, we had two rooms. There was the kitchen, with its window and the table where we ate and worked, and, behind the curtain, we had our bed, a lamp on the floor, and one of the plastic chairs from around the table. We had a bedroom. I began taking my time changing into my bed clothes at night. My mother did the same. A few weeks after we got the curtains, a woman from the council came to look at the damp on our ceiling, but when she saw our bedroom and the gold rope, she forgot about the damp. She started talking loudly. She said we were altering the property. She said the council would send us letters, so my mother pulled the curtains down in front of her and left them in piles on the floor. I took the rope. I put it inside my school rucksack under the bed.

When I was done with my poster, I moved the ladder to the window. It was quiet in our room after that. My mother was working at the table and I began washing the shirts she had finished. The soapy water in the sink came up above my elbows. I could hear my mother moving behind me. I could hear the rustle of silk under her hand, and the bangle on her wrist knocking the table when she pushed aside a sleeve or a hem. I lowered my arms further into the water. There was a pile of garments next to my mother's chair. The following morning, she would take three buses to another town, to a woman who would pay her for the garments and sell them on. And on Christmas Eve she would go again. I made a show of scrubbing the shirts in the sink. My shoulders hurt. I held the shirts under the water and pulled the plug. When I had finished rinsing and wringing, I pegged the shirts on the line my mother had strung from one end of the room to the other. I ignored the water dripping from the sleeves to the floor and took the next batch to the sink.

It was late by the time I lay down on the bed, but I knew I wouldn't sleep. And when my mother turned out the main light and climbed in next to me, I switched on the lamp and looked up at my poster. It was a good poster. The title, *Atalanta*, was printed in red sloping letters across the top. Underneath stood Atalanta the huntress, tall and still and calm as anything, while all around her the Calydonian hunters and their dogs crashed about and shook the air with such a spurious violence you could see things were unlikely to end well. Everything was white and gold, except Atalanta's bow and the tip of her arrow, which were red.

In the half-light, I felt my mother's arm against mine and heard her breathing. I turned onto my side. I could still hear her. I got up and sat at the table so that I could figure things out. After a few moments, my mother stirred.

'You need to eat?' she asked, low-voiced, from the bed.

I sometimes sat up at night when I wanted to think or when I was so hungry that everything was faintly throbbing—my chest, my heart, my head—and my mother would get up too, and she would warm some milk for me or she'd make me a rotlo on the stove with millet flour, dark and buttery. She would rest her head on her hand and watch me eat. Other times, when there was nothing to eat, she would just sit with me. It isn't possible to sleep off a hunger. It just isn't. And now that my mother had mentioned it, I felt the throbbing and knew I would be awake until morning. I thought of the rotlo, soft, hot off the stove.

'No, Mama,' I said. 'Go to sleep.'

My mother turned over and I looked at the poster again and tried to concentrate. On December 12th, the actors would arrive in Marlborough. They'd sell tickets and rehearse for a week and after that they'd perform their play every night for four nights, with their fifth and final performance, a matinée, on Christmas Eve. Before the final performance, they'd meet at the Crab House for their lunch, and that was when I'd approach them. I would tell their director I wished to join them as an actor. I'd give some sort of speech. The director, surprised and moved, would offer me a place in his company. And when the actors left Marlborough, I would go with them.

I had seen the actors going about the previous winter, and I'd slipped into the theatre on the evening of their first performance. The curtains had opened and in the warm hush of the auditorium I saw them make palaces and forests out of nothing. Their eyes darkened with love and shone with all the tempers of the world. Everything about them was bright and shimmering, even their boots glinted like fleeting thoughts as they moved about the stage. Afterwards they looked so different, laughing together outside the Crab House, that it was impossible to forget them. I lay my head on the kitchen table and let my eyes close. In five days, they would be here. Five days. I began to feel the pressure of it, like a good tight ball inside my stomach.

The next morning, it snowed. It was Sunday. My mother and I looked at one another, and without a word we put on our coats and went out. The streetlamps were palely lit, and the sky was thick and almost pink. Snowflakes swirled about our heads. Our cheeks were flushed but it wasn't all that cold and so we walked with our coats open. My mother was looking up and I saw she was smiling, and then I was smiling too. I couldn't help myself. The snow kept falling, and we were lightheaded with it.

We were passing by Mrs Wyndham's shop when my mother decided we would go inside. I thought of my poster, that I'd stolen, and suggested we go to the other shops by the pier, where they knew us.

'We are here,' my mother said warmly, as if she was agreeing with me, and put her hand on the door.

No one had seen me with the poster, I knew that, but when we stepped inside and the bell on the shop door dinged, I felt my heart thumping a little.

Mrs Wyndham was busy behind the counter taking money, wrapping parcels, talking the whole time to her customers who stood in a line before her.

Her white hands were twisting string round and round a brown paper parcel. Inside were tins of syrup, jam, bottled sardines. It was hard to tell where all the bottles and tins had come from because when you looked around, the shelves were nearly empty. And they were covered with dust. The whole place was shabby, even the tired strands of tinsel that might otherwise have suggested good cheer. If Mrs Wyndham accused me, I thought, I would deny it. I didn't know what my mother would say but I thought that with the snow falling like it was and everything turning soft and white outside, Mrs Wyndham could turn to her and enquire, Isn't that poster, at this very moment, on the ceiling above your bed?, and my mother would look at me, and then she would look out, and she would answer: No. It isn't.

The queue had been moving quickly and now we were at the front. Behind us, the line was hushed. My mother was speaking. I had learned to pay attention when my mother spoke because people didn't always take kindly to what she said.

'It is baked today?' she was asking.

Mrs Wyndham stared at my mother and then she leaned her elbows on the counter and looked questioningly at me, as if I might translate.

I felt my cheeks grow hot.

'Was it baked today?' I said.

Mrs Wyndham straightened.

'All our food is fresh,' she said, and turned to the woman next to us in the line. She didn't want to serve my mother and no one was saying anything about it. The woman approached the counter and ordered two large rashers, and Mrs Wyndham smiled briefly, lifted a large body of meat onto the counter, and began slicing. I saw that she didn't know about the poster, and it didn't seem to matter now.

I tried to take hold of my mother's hand but my mother stepped forward. She pointed at a floury loaf on the shelf behind Mrs Wyndham.

'Please,' she said. 'One bloomer.'

Mrs Wyndham stopped slicing.

She took the loaf below the one my mother had indicated, placed it on the counter, wrapped it slowly.

My mother was looking at Mrs Wyndham's hands. There was no expression on her face. She watched Mrs Wyndham's fingers that were shiny from the meat, and she said nothing, but she paid for the bread and when we got home she broke it in two and tossed the contaminated half onto the frozen mud outside our building.

Later, around five, when my mother was lying down, I went out there, found the bread, ate it. I walked around for a bit and after I came back in, turned out the light and lay next to my mother. And I thought: *four days*.

Since there was no school, I spent these days helping my mother, and when there wasn't too much sewing or washing or ironing to do, I wandered the town. I went by the Crab House and though there was no one around I stood on the pavement outside as if I were in a queue. For long stretches I sat on the sea wall in the freezing cold, thinking. The sea was the same as it always was, mostly a pale, washed-out grey rising and falling under a colourless sky. When I joined the actors, there would be other skies. There would be other seas. At home, my mother told me I would catch a fever. Her head was bent over the hem she was sewing and she said it without looking up, her mouth half-closed over the pins she held between her lips. I put the light on for her and went out. There were icicles now, above shop windows, and ice on the pavements. By early evening, the sky was black and there were pockets of light: coloured bulbs dipping over the roads at intervals, red, green, blue; a scattering of stars. I stood outside the Crab House until my face was burning with cold and I could almost hear the heels of the actors' boots cracking distant ice as they approached our town.

My mother kept working, and I kept on with my chores, and when at last the actors came, I approached Sally Martin, whose father managed the theatre. I gave her a rose-pink purse with silver threading that I had made over the summer, and in return she gave me the key to a disused room high up over the auditorium. It was no more than a cupboard really, filled with boxes and pipes and electronic equipment, but it had a small window looking down onto the stage, and when I stood close to the window I could see and hear everything. I dropped my rucksack and waited.

The actors gathered below me, all dressed up. I could feel my heart beating in the dark. On that first afternoon I watched them rehearse the entire play. The cast members who weren't performing at any one time were at the back or sides of the stage, assembling mountains and skies, hammering nails into wood. There was Atalanta, the virgin—abandoned by her father, nursed by a bear, fair as the snow and swift-footed as the wind—on a stool behind the

Chorus, erecting a tree. There was the Calydonian Boar, sent by the goddess Artemis to ravage the land, whose front and back, a man and a woman, were re-painting the tops of billowing clouds. There were the hunters, who made a great racket and botched things until Atalanta sailed in on a foaming sea; the Fates; the Messengers; Meleager, who loved Atalanta and would murder his uncles for her sake. Amidst all the landscaping and woodwork, I glimpsed Meleager's face in the floodlights, disfigured with grief and remorse, and in the next moment the lights dimmed and he was turning up his shirtsleeves, nodding eagerly at something the director was saying. It was all so strange and wonderful that I wanted to cry. I stood in the cupboard quietly watching and didn't leave until the actors had gone.

It was dark outside when I wandered up into town. The night was still. In the windows of the closed-down department store, I saw myself passing. I saw my whole figure, from my white face to my muddy boots. I slowed down. In an instant, I was transformed so that anyone watching would see, reflected in the department store windows, Atalanta the virgin stalking a wild boar amid the green hills of Calydon. The virgin adjusted her rucksack. Slowly, she drew her bow; she let her arrow fly. And then she held her stance. When the one who loved her laid the spoils at her feet and I caught in the air the echo of her faint, chaste laugh and saw in the department store window the rosy blush in her cheek, I was ready to hear cries of *ah!* and *bravo!* and a volley of applause. There was silence. The street was empty and the sky was gloomy and low, but I looked up at the Christmas lights, and knew I wasn't alone.

I returned to the theatre the next day and the next day and the next. I repeated all of the actors' lines. Before long, I knew in advance what they would say and I mouthed the words as they did. I stood at that cupboard window for hours. Once, when I had been standing the whole afternoon and the air was heavy and warm, I rested my head on a pipe and closed my eyes and soon the actors were no longer below me on the stage. They were standing in the cupboard with me, speaking directly into my living soul.

… *What storm is this that tightens all our sail?*…

… *What shall be done with all these tears of ours?*…

… *What shall we say now? what thing comes of us?*…

… *What shall be said?*…

Somewhere far back in my mind, I was thinking that I would have to tell my mother she must remember to go over and close Mr Levy's windows.

*

The opening night was a success. The whole audience stood up to applaud. I walked home knowing that the actors would have a good time wherever they went that evening. I hadn't yet seen the actors around town and when I tried to imagine them there, among the holiday lights, dressed in their everyday clothes, I felt an ache inside me.

The second performance was different in some way, and during the third performance, I could see from my cupboard that something was wrong. It was Atalanta. She was forgetting her lines. She left the stage when she should have been speaking. Sally Martin told me Atalanta was sick with food poisoning. I asked her if they would send her home.

'What home?' Sally replied, and I understood that the actors only had each other, and I thought that was good, that was enough.

On the fourth night, it was someone else playing Atalanta. One of the messengers. A boy. He stumbled about and the actors gave one another looks. Seeing their anxious faces below me, I wanted to bang my fists on the cupboard window, shout down: *Hail thou! Good news!* But I knew I wasn't up to it, and in the end the boy didn't do too badly. I watched from above the stage and afterwards I walked along the sea wall. I had never imagined the director might give me the leading role, not right away, because how could he? But as I walked up to town, towards the department store, I started to feel that everything was possible. In the store's huge windows, I studied my face. I began reciting Atalanta's lines.

When I returned home that evening, my mother was sitting at the table in the dark, looking out of our window. There was a smell of burning from the oat biscuits she had forgotten. I put the light on, opened the window, and ate the rice and yogurt she had left for me, then cleared my plate away. There were clothes all over the floor and on the bed. Nothing was ready. I began washing shirts and my mother lay down for a while before getting up again to sit at the table. I hung the shirts on the line.

'Mama,' I said when the line was full. 'Did you eat?' I was rubbing my arms with a towel but they just seemed to stay damp.

My mother turned her head to me. When I went over and knelt at her feet, she smiled absently and touched my arm, and then she moved her hand away and murmured, 'Where is your towel?'

I caught her hand, held it.

'I won't always be here,' I told her.

I won't be here tomorrow.

'You have to take care, Mama. You have to eat. Do you understand?'

We both looked at our cupboards, the half packet of rice, the few tins. I thought of Mrs Wyndham's empty shelves and all her jars and bottles that appeared from nowhere and I felt tears coming. I didn't know how I could rehearse the speech I was to give the actors, all that 'as it were' and 'if there be' and 'what thing is this'. I was sweating and my head was beginning to hurt. I got up and brought the towel, knelt there while my mother held it to my forehead and my arms. I leaned into her. I could feel her warmth, her slow breaths rising and falling with mine. She smelled of biscuits and silk. I saw she would pull away, and when she did, I felt a rush of cool air on my skin, and she was gazing out of the window again. I didn't move. I wanted her to look at me. I wanted her to explain to me about Mrs Wyndham, and why we had nothing. I wanted her to tell me that it didn't matter, that we were okay, that she was okay. But it was no use, because what she was looking at was an absence so vast that it consumed her.

I stood up, went to the window. It had been raining. The pavement was wet and dark. I rested an arm lightly across my stomach. This was how my mother stood when she was thinking about my father. I had believed for a long time that the two of us—my mother and I—had disappointed my father. There was not enough life in us. Mainly, it was my mother, it must have been, because back then I was only a baby and I couldn't be blamed. I believed all this until I was seven, which was when I met a man on the beach who recognised me because I looked so much like my mother. I'd found a whole portion of chips on the pier, wrapped in newspaper. The chips were good; vinegary and soft. I was sat on the wall facing the sea, pushing the chips into my mouth, breathing out from time to time as if the chips were too hot, when this man came up and asked me about my mother. Since I had this whole feast on my lap and the sun was setting and it was warm and the sea was a riot, dirty green and wild, I shifted a bit, made a space for this man. The man was dark, darker than my mother. He wore a suit. He sat down and removed his hat, held it on his lap. He talked. He told me I might not think I looked like my mother, but I did. He told me he had known my mother back home. I should have seen her when she was young, he said.

Back home, he said, she had been the life of the whole town. She made things happen. She only had to walk past and something wonderful would happen. And it wasn't just that. The man turned his hat slowly, over and over in his hands. She looked out for you, he said. You knew that if you were lonely or in trouble, she would notice. I'd stopped eating. I turned a bit so I could see his face. He was looking up at the sky and there were grains of sand stuck to his cheeks. Oh, he said. His eyes were shining.

I began asking this man about my father, but he became so worked up and disoriented that I had to stop. What had happened, I realised, was that my father had come along, out of the sea or wherever he came from with his thick wet beard and his hungry mouth, and he loved my mother because of those things the man had mentioned. My mother's people cast her out in shame. My mother was not ashamed. She let my father hold her. She let him carry her away. She let him bring her here. And maybe it had all gone fine to begin with, but slowly my father had eaten all the joy out of my mother and then, one day, seeing what he had done, he left.

After I saw the actors, I imagined myself on a stage in another town. A midnight performance, where the audience would stand under a late summer moon. I would be gazing into the rapt, moonlit faces of the audience and my father would be there in the middle, his eyes shining, like this man on the beach. He might be old by then. A different person. I would address him anyway. I would assure him that I was not going to let another human being eat the joy out of me. And maybe later I would tell him he wasn't the only one who could leave.

My mother and I got ready for bed. I climbed in next to her, thinking it was all over. I could not leave her. Our arms touched. I stared at my poster, seeing not Atalanta with her red-tipped arrow, but my mother, gazing out of our window at nothing, and then Mrs Wyndham slicing meat on her counter, wrapping our bread with her greasy hands, the bread that I did not want but that I had eaten. I closed my eyes but Mrs Wyndham was still there, offering me a full jar of syrup, the darkest, sweetest sort, and I was getting my fingers into the sweetest part at the bottom of the jar. I felt a slow, jabbing pain in my side, like a hard stone. I turned onto my stomach, but it was no good. I kicked the blanket off me. I waited with the pain inside me until my mother was asleep. I got up, ducked under the line with the shirts. At the window I looked out, and all I could think of was the actors leaving Marlborough without me, and I knew I could not stay.

*

It was Christmas Eve. I thought my mother would need to rest, but she rose when she heard me getting things ready for her to take on the bus. I removed the shirts and other garments from the line, and she ironed the ones that weren't completely dry while I sat on the bed, folding and putting everything in a bag for her. She opened her purse and gave me a coin for the loaf cake we would have on Christmas day. I was still sitting on the bed. I looked at the coin and thought: *When she walks out of our door, I will not see her again.*

'Mama.'

I stood up. She turned.

I just looked at her.

She came to me and I held the coin and she put her hand on my forehead. She touched my hair. *Make something happen*, I thought. Her breath was soft and warm.

'Stay home today. You feel hot,' she said. 'And tomorrow we will have cake.' Maybe she had some dim, passing presentiment of a new absence because for two seconds, three seconds, she stood near me. And then she turned away to find her gloves and left.

It was already late. I got my rucksack from under the bed and took out the gold curtain rope. I had on the loose navy tunic I wore for school. I gathered the sleeves onto my shoulders, twisted the rope around my waist. On the rope, I hung a small pouch made of leather and inside it put the coin my mother had given me. I pulled on my boots, tied them with new laces, and went to brush my teeth at the sink. My mother had left her bangle on the draining board. I looked at the door, and then I had the bangle in my hands, and I was turning it, pushing it over my knuckle and onto my wrist. It felt strange. I pretended to wipe the worktop in order to hear the knocking sound, but there was nothing. I took it off, left it by the sink.

Once I'd packed my rucksack, I put it back under the bed. I would come and get it once I had agreed things with the actors. I thought that before I left for good, I would go across the hall to Mr Levy. I would put notes on his windows, and I'd tell him everything. Maybe some part of him would understand and he would remember. There was still a letter to write, for my mother. I thought of her sitting on one bus, and then another. There was time. I would do it later.

I pulled the door closed after me and the whole corridor was quiet. There was no sound at all. I adjusted my rope and stepped out the front door. The air outside was freezing. I walked fast, taking the back paths instead of going along the sea wall.

The actors were already queueing in the street outside the Crab House when I came up the road. They were talking together, gesturing wildly, laughing. They were all there: the hunters, the Calydonian boar, front and back, the Fates, all of them. They were dressed in their everyday clothes, their pale, unlit faces both familiar and extraordinary above the upturned collars of their winter coats. I felt like I might shout out, seeing them like that, but I just joined the queue and, after briefly noticing me, they continued their conversations.

The company director was tall. His skin had a bluish tone, and he kept blowing on his hands. In the performance, he did not have a speaking part. He was Iasius the Arcadian, Atalanta's father, who desired a son and abandoned his unwanted daughter on a mountaintop.

'Sir,' I said.

He glanced at me over his cupped hands.

'I'd like to join your company,' I said. 'I'd like to take the part of Atalanta.'

There was the laughter I expected from the actors in the queue, but the director did not laugh. He lowered his hands.

'I saw you practising,' he said. He nodded towards the department store. I stared at him.

'I know it isn't really about all that,' I said. 'I mean, I know acting isn't about... '

'What is it about?' he asked. He wasn't smiling. He truly wanted me to tell him.

I felt tearful and became aware that I was shivering. I said, 'I don't know.'

The director nodded thoughtfully. The queue moved forward a little.

'Get on, child,' said a large man, plump and bald, whom I knew as the Chorus of Calydonian Maidens.

I turned to him, shivering so much now that I thought he would hear my teeth chattering, and he grinned, raising an expectant eyebrow at me, as if he were looking forward to hearing what I had to say. But only when I had the whole company's attention did I begin speaking, my voice full and clear, not like an actor's but like a woman beseeching a throng of guilty men.

> '... if toward any of you I am overbold
> That take thus much upon me, let him think
> How I, for all my forest holiness,

Fame, and this armed and iron maidenhood,
Pay thus much also; I shall have no man's love
For ever, and no face of children born
Or feeding lips upon me or fastening eyes
… but a cold and sacred life, but strange,
But far from dances and the back-blowing torch,
Far off from flowers or any bed of man,
Shall my life be for ever: me the snows
That face the first o' the morning, and cold hills
Full of the land-wind and sea-travelling storms —'

I went on for two minutes without intermission, and when I was done, Atalanta of Arcadia's words hung in the air. The actors in the queue were watching me but, ignoring them all, I faced the director.

He stared at the pavement, as if he were making a decision. It seemed a long time before he raised his eyes to me.

He asked, 'Do you know the whole thing?'

I nodded.

'Yes,' he said, slowly. 'I think you do.'

I looked at his good, grave face, at this man who understood everything, this man who was going to save me, and I wanted to fall at his feet. And then I heard, as if from a great distance, the ugly roar of the Chorus's laughter. It was hard, indifferent, and it was meant to shame me, and it did. I turned away, feeling upset and confused, and that was when I saw my mother coming up the road on the opposite side. My heart slipped.

I moved closer to the window, so that the director was blocking me. But he stepped to one side to follow my gaze and, doing so, put me back in my mother's line of sight.

The door to Mrs Wyndham's shop opened.

I heard Mrs Wyndham pouring the watery contents of a bucket into the road.

I heard the director's voice.

'Isn't that your mother?' he was saying.

The Chorus swivelled around, his whole big bulk, to stare at my mother, and then, appalled, at me.

It was cold. It was freezing. The thick dark hairs on my arms—dark like hers—stood upright. I wished I had worn something else, something to cover me. My mouth opened, and I felt my legs give way. I began to sink.

That was when my mother looked over.

She saw everything. Her big eyes seemed to hang on to me. The director put a hand on my shoulder and somehow he was holding me up.

He asked again, roughly, 'Isn't that your mother?'

The whole street was quiet.

'No,' I said. 'It isn't.'

The director's shirt was white, so white it hurt my eyes staring at it. The pocket needed stitching; I could fix it in a few minutes, I thought. I knew he wasn't looking at me. He was looking at my mother. When he let me go, he moved towards the open door of the Crab House. The others were all inside by then.

At the doorway, he stopped. He looked over his shoulder.

'Are you coming in?' he asked.

Inside, the door closed softly behind me.

The windows were all steamed up and there was the smell of frying and beer. The place was noisy with talk. Everywhere, spoons clinked loudly in soup bowls. The director was at the counter. I saw in front of him a line of crabs piled in close to one another, half in and half out of their shells. I heard him checking the time and ordering whelks. The girl behind the counter asked me what I wanted. I looked at all the claws and bones and eyes displayed on ice in the glass cabinets in front of me—pinky orange, white, silver—and my stomach turned.

'The same,' I said and slipped my fingers into the leather pouch at my waist. I found the coin, held it, hot, inside the pouch.

I put the coin on the counter.

The director and I stood there not speaking, until the girl handed us a large greasy cone each, heaped with thick, still, yellow things that I supposed were the whelks. A wooden fork was sticking out of one of them.

The director sat next to the Chorus and I took the stool opposite. The Chorus kept his small, watchful eyes on his soup, dipping his head to his spoon, swallowing delicately. The director was watching his actors. He did not move, nor did he speak. I looked at my cone.

'A bad business,' the Chorus said into his soup, deeply, wonderingly, in the awful way you say a thing you know you're going to repeat often.

The cone with my whelks looked huge and terrible. I pulled out the wooden fork, stuck it into a new whelk. It met resistance. I forced it in. I heard the director saying something and someone answering. I raised the fork, pushed the whelk between my teeth. There was the sudden overwhelming taste of the sea. The thing was large and slimy inside my mouth, like another tongue. I bit into it. It was firm, not quite rubbery. I kept chewing it and it would not reduce. The director passed me a cup of water. I drank half, swallowing the thing down.

The Chorus spoke again. He didn't look up, but he was waiting. He knew he had been heard and he wanted me to answer. I didn't know if it was for my sake or his own that he wanted me to speak. I could have answered. I could have stood up. I could have told him about Mrs Wyndham's bread and her hands and the curtains on the floor and the emptiness. I could have told him what I had felt in the auditorium when I first saw the actors up on the stage. I could have told him about my father and how it is that one person can come to blot out another. I looked at the Chorus's bowed head and I thought that when I answered, it would be to my mother, who would keep on with her sewing. There was only water left in the Chorus's bowl and he continued spooning it into his mouth, and I hated him. I hated him as unconditionally as if it had been he who had denied my mother and not I.

Someone stood up, and everyone began finishing their drinks, pushing their bowls away, scraping stools. The director stood too. He came around the table, stopped at my side. He put a hand on my shoulder and said, 'Our company is full.'

At the doorway, he paused, and said without turning, 'But I think you know how to act.'

And he left.

And I kept sitting there.

There was nobody at the counter and nobody came over to clear up. When I went outside, the street was empty. I crossed over, stood in front of the department store windows, feeling weak and dizzy. I could smell whatever mess Mrs Wyndham had poured into the road, and there was that flatness about the world because everything bright was obscured.

When I opened my mouth, the cold air froze my breath.

The department store windows went black.

Everything went black.

And I was on a spotlit stage, all set up to look like Mr Levy's place, and Mr Levy was there, and I was closing his windows and repeating my lines. But

I wasn't really on the stage. I was up in the cupboard-sized room high above the stage.

'I'm afraid,' I was telling Mr Levy.

'Sometimes you can think too much,' he replied.

I waited, but that was all he had.

I rested my head on a pipe. I was so tired.

We were quiet a long time, and then somehow we were outside the Crab House. Mr Levy held his hands at his sides. I cried a little. We both looked up. The sky was a dark milky blue and our breath was suspended in front of us.

'I'm afraid,' I told Mr Levy.

'I know,' he said.

The first stars appeared above us and I looked back into the Crab House: the empty bowls; the wet, balled-up napkins; the discarded bones. I saw my father gorging himself like some heart-swallowing giant. His hands were big blocks, indiscriminate and mesmerising, the wooden fork insignificant in his hands, and then it wasn't him, it was me, and I was forking whelks and pushing them into my mouth, swallowing them down. But I already knew. It was me. I was the one who had fed until my mother became tired and sick.

The lights came up and the director, walking past, blew on his hands and told me I had my cue.

'I'm afraid,' I told Mr Levy.

'I know,' he said, and he began climbing his ladder, with its two loose rungs. It was propped against the department store windows and I was standing beside it. The soft black soles of Mr Levy's boots filled my vision. His climbing went on forever, and instead of going up, Mr Levy was going back and back and back. The department store windows were open and Mr Levy was way back inside and from there he was speaking.

His breath arrived first. Slow, shuddering, pale blue bursts that expanded and filled the sky. But when the sound came, it wasn't speech, it was a deafening cry, lonely and deep and thunderous, and the department store windows began to shake, and the windows of the Crab House and the shops and the houses. And I was crouching against the wall, covering my ears, watching Mr Levy's breath that was turning the sky into something else, and I saw that it was only fog and the awful, lonely sound was a fog horn from some ship beyond the sea wall. But across the street, the director was waiting, and so, slowly, I rose to my feet, put my shoulders back, and opened my lungs to answer—

'South'

After the memoir by Ernest Shackleton

The geologist suppressed all thought of rocks.
On a flat piece of ice, two hundred yards long and fifty wide,
the whiteness of breaking water surged around him.
He was not altogether without material.
Pebbles found in penguins were of interest
as were blocks of ice so neatly laid
it seemed impossible for them to be Nature's work.
Bergs under pressure emitted noises:
the geologist heard tapping as from a hammer,
electric trams, birds singing, kettles boiling.

Field: ice of such extent that its limits cannot be seen from the masthead.
Brash: the wreck of other kinds of ice.
The only dry things on board were swollen mouths and burning tongues.
When they were not on watch they lay in each other's arms
and their frozen suits thawed where their bodies met,
huddled in the laden, spray-swept boats,
the beards even of the younger men might have been those of patriarchs,
for the frost and the salt spray had made them white.
When the time came to march,
holes were dug in the snow, and into these white graves
was consigned much of sentimental value: private letters, the ship's Bible
but not before the geologist tore out the fly-leaf
bearing Queen Alexandra's writing and the verse from Job
Out of whose womb came the ice?

Danielle McLaughlin

*Note: An earlier version of this poem was exhibited in Bantry last summer as part of the
Museum of Miniature at West Cork Arts Centre, having been commissioned as a response to
the miniature by Sharon Whooley on the facing page.*

Sharon Whooley: *Untitled*

A Woman Of Thirty

Aoife Casby

This dog-eared Balzac book, I scribble all over it. Notes like:

[*numbers control the world.*]

Now there's a silly statement. I've never known a numerologist, someone who scours lives for patterns but, if I did, could I take him seriously?

And more recently: [*my breath is dazing up the windscreen, the book seems closer to me because of it.*]

And: [*once upon a time…*]

… since I think that I can tell a story, I will begin as if it were a fairy tale. Fairy tales are alarming little jewels. I'm not the first person to know this. From the dark things that almost happen to people and the darker things that do happen. Which part of the *once*? Which part of the *upon*? *Once*, like it happened on a definite day, when the grass was arranging its narrative and the sky behind the sun was the blue cause of it all, and my tininess part of an intimidating whole. Say a once in 1992 or, perhaps, almost ten weeks ago. *Upon* gives *once* reality, delivers the once into this terribly physical world. *A* is indefinite, nebulous, or perhaps simply imagination; and *Time*, the great ineluctable, the chilling dynamic of it all. *Once upon a time…* But this is no fairy tale. It's real.

[*she is in your margins*
and she is you;
this opening is, of course,
a diversionary tactic,
she cannot yet listen.]

My Tom had many stories from his childhood and I liked them better than mine. When he was young nothing happened in his family that didn't have water associated with it—a flood, a burst pipe, an overflowing toilet. His father broke his leg on the way home from work, caught in a flash downpour, lucky he wasn't drowned; one Christmas when there were thirteen cousins in their farmhouse, the toilet overflowed and they all had to use a hole that was dug at the bottom of the back yard; and all that laughter; pipes exploded in winter, rusting parts splintered apart in summer; plugholes blocked, flat rooves caved in under unseasonal torrents. A vase smashed on the floor. Holy water scattered on the doorstep. Slipping into shallow cataract pools across green slimed rocks. Water, not just as a background to the broken legs and births and funerals and happinesses, but as a central character. His words. *Central character.* Since I like those stories better, I have made Tom's childhood my own.

[*she can't make*
any more mistakes. she cannot
make a family that will laugh
together. that would smother
her…]

So here, beside the steering wheel, I make Tom's childhood story part of my own growing up.

[*funny anecdotes, definitely not*
true, to tell the kids.
always did her best,
too,
given
the
circum-
stances.]

I want to have a home. I practise deafness. I have been living in this car for just over five weeks and no longer continually watch myself in the rear-view mirror. Me—I am autumnal. Burnished long hair, coffee-ish, like a red squirrel, round face, hazel eyes. I do not like that thing in my stomach that is almost the starved horror of first love, a tightness, a tangle of inexplicable disquiet. I have long fingers and am quite small, flat-bellied, slightly largish thighs, faded but visible tan lines. Yes, I fell out of love with sex a little while ago. Not because it wasn't pleasurable, charming or humorous, but because it forgot about me. I had a lot of love in me. I had. Sex in a car though. I don't love the gracelessness of it. Things spilling and hurting. I prefer to masturbate if the urge hits me at all. Easier.

[*she will need the lessons of myth.*
other people's stories will tell her
who she is. but there are some
truths she does not want to hear.]

This book that I leave on the dashboard at night is Balzac's *A Woman of Thirty*. The main character, Julie, is a fairly clever woman, disappointed with sex, who makes questionable, strange choices all over the place and who listens to others more than she should. I try hard to imagine her dilapidated breath, the crying, when I read her story. I close my eyes and conjure the subtle flame of her breathing on my neck, hear her swish into the safety or dreadful confinement of a room and stifle a sigh, her eyes bright with belief and expectation. [*she needs to be able to open the windows, the doors, but that lets in the cold.*] I scribble here in the margins of the book and try to ignore how the interior of a car stifles sounds. I stir her voice with scribbles and whispers so that I will hear what she has to say, what her writer didn't allow her to say. I can hear her hardly recognisable voice, the resilient tone of it. When I open my eyes to scratch these thoughts in those mean borders, the ghost of her stays beside me for a few seconds, enough to get through a few more pages. I mean, I don't have an unhappy marriage like her, and Julie, well this whole thing, her story, ends up like a bad TV series.

[*there was a vicious tearing when*
her soul seemed to pass into his
through demented love. you
should know. the horror of love.]

Tom gave the Balzac to me. He did this now and again. Strange gifts. He said, 'I saw the green of the cover and the faded spine and the ruined pages kind of peeping out and I thought of you. Look MDCCCXCVII'

What was I meant to make of that? I thought of mouldy sandwiches, all the deep naming. But I loved that book and that I couldn't understand the way he saw me. But. I love that book. I love the justified text of the pages. It's easy on the eye and kind of invites the edges. There is space for her, space for me. But sometimes there's too much space for thinking. In the margins of the book, I talk to her, to Julie; she allows me to think. I think she wants me to be with her, I think she may talk back. Maybe I am her.

[*but*]

Until recent days, nobody has looked into the car long enough to see the strangeness and wonder. The car is not warm. My sleeping bag is dampish on the outside.

> [*here,*
> *she feels fear in her stomach*
> *and sometimes cries,*
> *insensible tears, doesn't feel*
> *relief.*]

I'd like to have a house that had more hallways than rooms. The going from one room to another is a mundane walk that is much overlooked; being in that threshold space, the place in the home where the least change occurs; where there are the same side tables that were perhaps in your grandmother's house, now doing their duty here, or the two pictures on the walls that no one remembers buying and would be stretched to describe if asked, and the light switches where the family fingers encounter one another's prints. Hallways.

> [*and there are conceptions about*
> *vaginas,*
> *words that are important*
> *like 'unknown', 'roomy', 'flesh',*
> *'tenebrous', 'impelling'*
> *and that sort of thing,*
> *but perhaps this is not the place.*]

Wednesday, a security guard loitered up and down behind the car. I could feel his doubt and the professional shyness in his walk. I don't think he'll try to talk to me. I wish he would. I imagine him at home, telling his wife and daughters about this woman who has made her bed up in the back of the car and the sad way she has pushed forward the driver and passenger seat for night time and moves her car furniture back and sits up front during the day when she's not gone about town. I imagine him narrating me. 'She seems very nice,' he says. 'She reads. I see a book on the dash.'

> [*huh! mistakes she made early on.*
> *after hours of sitting, not driving,*
> *the insistent hug of the car seat is*
> *uncomfortable, too close. r*
> *emember all the times laying on*
> *the couch, large thighs splayed*

across his. that spongy feeling.
that satisfied sigh.]

Outside, across the movie-shot car park, beyond the craned building site of the hospital, in the angry fields, there's a coloured tempest building up, the fat belly of it flouncing around and finding its voice, an orange or a yellow wind warning, I'm not sure which. I wasn't concentrating. Half-heard broadcasts from the small staticky pocket radio. The background. The car battery didn't last long with the radio on. Those notes are not in the manual. I will have to sell the car eventually. The wind though. Of course it's the globe warming up and cooling down in all the wrong places and losing balance in itself like a room where the radiator is on and the window open, or a womb where the margin is on the inside, not the outside, and it's all our own fault.

What did she say, the weather lady and her atmospheric tone? Listening to the wind whine outside the car, I hear a huge red heifer panicking.

I'm tired. My dreams are tired. My smile is tired. And I don't know people anymore. I understand it now when they say that if you tell your story it lessens the burden of it. I feel a need. Maybe in writing down these words in the margins something will change.

[*is it her fault? her father told her*
that women fall in love with an
imaginary creature, that man of
their choice and, too late, fate. she
meets this illusion she created,
sees it turn into an odious
skeleton. she is not wrong. but.]

It felt as if I should be writing our story in the margins of this book, outlining the present state of affairs, but I don't think I'm able to deal with thematic requirements, to delineate the problem. I know elements of the structure of my story—the exposition, the necessary rising action, the climax, the denouement. It's like writing up a shelf-life analysis: the words should tell you where to go with the food, in easy steps, and my story has all the elements. The structure is lifelike. Exposed. Conflicted. But really, the beginning of life is hazardous. It's supposed to be safe in the room—womb. Isn't it? Shouldn't it be? Me and Tom made a beginning. It's funny how womb sounds like room.

But.

I'm single at the moment. Before Tom there had been a patchy but egalitarian list: a scrupulous financial advisor, two accountants, a reporter who moaned aloud in the passive voice when he was about to come, one or three teachers, a French-speaking street sweeper. Painful and deliberate endings.

I am currently unemployed. I didn't expect not to be able to renew my contract. The fact that the idea of permanence was an illusion makes me feel very unsteady. Inside, I am job hunting, imagining myself applying for the few openings I glance at online. My heart isn't in it.

Initially the unemployment did not worry me but now, damp sleeping-bagged feet resting on the brake and clutch, I'm not so sure.

If things were different and I wasn't living in an Opel Corsa, it would be a good time to plan that European adventure, or try to become a chef—someone who makes the food rather than analyses it to un-enjoyment.

> [*ha! scribble the dreams. you are a woman who has only known the joy of love in fucked dreams, whose future is curled up like a torpid snake.*]

Tom and I are no longer together. I am getting used to it. But.

There really is a storm on the way. I feel the grey sky talking to me through the roof with the Rorschach coffee stains from that time I drove Tom to the sea and we stopped for petrol and drinks and I went too fast over the speed ramps. Seagulls have begun shitting haphazardly on the windscreen. I could do with a warm coffee and I need to charge the laptop again soon. This means I have to sit in a café, which isn't a bad thing. I need to see people smile and sigh and look at me. But it means I have to count my pennies.

My breath makes traces on the air that never form into anything I can understand.

Tom said when he met me that he knew his life was going to be different. He got that the wrong way around.

The cranes are like ghosts this morning. I like this luminescent mist. I did a bungee jump once off a crane, a lot higher than the starved-looking metal giraffes hauling that hospital into existence. There is a 'before-the-bungee-jump me' and an 'improbable after-the-bungee-jump me'. I would have expected the after one to be less afraid of life. She ought to be the type who wouldn't be afraid in a car park overnight. But.

I like to delve into magazines I would never buy, the ones that I find in waiting rooms, and I still never pass up the opportunity to talk to anyone selling an idea on the street.

Yes. I used to cry a lot. And I am familiar with the self-complacent concerns of loneliness.

I met Tom before the bungee jump.

I have been showering and toileting and swimming at Tom's gym, the place beside the hospital. That couples' membership will soon run out.

[*her cleverness may not get her out of this. her dishonesty got her into that. she will have to feign bravery she no longer feels. needing another is awful.*]

The nocturnal inside of a car is like an incubator for all the strange thoughts that usually go to sleep—the thoughts that need sleep. I've been contemplating the implications of 2.5ish cm. I've been contemplating coincidence. I measured the margins in this book. It's about 2.5ish cm. It's the space and time in which the future must know the past. That empty space has to be enough to contain the ghosts and blood that slide into it. Intention inhabits what we can't see.

Yes, there is time in those spacious corridors between sections on the page, and at the beginning lines of paragraphs. From room to room to room. Time and ideas are plumbed and dying in those spaces. But this means that there is another life in the margins and living in the indents. I like the page. All the words I sketch could drag the guts of the unsaid into the hungriness of the margins. The shape of the air in this car is a drowsy blanket.

[*when 'horror' and 'happiness' appear in the same sentence you know there is a story.*]

This scribbling is not producing anything. I write something there in the margin, left or right, something vulgar or true or something to reveal myself to me. Or scribble in a kooky little picture, a hopeful doodle of a wish, like a child's drawing of a house and the stick family in all its shattering pieces. Or, I think that it is infinitely harder to look out than in.

Or, That's a problem.

[*or, it's ugly and grey being alone even if you choose it.*]

[*or, 2.5ish cm is a capacity of something small.*]

Or, Tom and I were together for nearly five years.

[*or, she wished for a family. no more than anyone else. no less either.*]

Or, Simply a whole story. Like—

Little Red Riding Hood. That wolf in the bed. The awful realisation. Is Granny dead, in his belly, under the bed? Is there a woodsman? Does Granny run? Is there an axe? That moment in the bedroom, and Granny's teeth. It's like the daylight has been taken out of existence. Think about that, '… all the better to eat you with!' and I'm terrified. Granny's gone. Death and fear are the event everywhere you look. I never hear the end of the story. I know that Granny wins, but for me it is with the fear and the death that the story resides; the wicked wolf has all the cunning power. The story never concludes. [*what an appalling way to begin a childhood.*]

My story: I'm alone. And I realise it.

> [*there are thousands of babies'*
> *bones buried in loose dirt pits*
> *all over the country, bones*
> *constantly being separated*
> *from their flesh and*
> *the idea of their flesh.*]

I am a creature.

His character, Julie; Balzac didn't know her so well. I'm not sure he listened to her.

Me and Tom had a conversation about kids and the future. I consider myself a bang-up listener and worked on being present with him. It was a cosy talk: duvets, open window, early summer birds. All eye contact and fingertips. The conversation about the kids meandered from the financial structures that would have to be in place to the restraint on lifestyle that would occur and all the little choices we would intelligently make in between. I leaned my head on his shoulder in a very clichéd magazine-spread way.

> [*she is happy today;*
> *will her happiness last?*]

We laughed about the mini-me fantasies and how we could take our kids hill-walking and to feed the ducks and that I would be better helping them to understand basic mathematical concepts but then, he said 'kids' as if he was reacting to me deliberately, squeezing the ketchup right on the tablecloth in a big bloody splodge… I suppose there was an unresolvedness about it that I, perhaps, didn't tabulate and put away correctly.

My father disappeared from our lives when I was seven. It both is and is not the trauma that you think. He was a big man. Kind I think. Woolly jumpers. Corduroys. Lots of brown and green.

*[was the man she chose
ever father material?]*

I have a shadow of my father in some of the images that mug my thinking.
    You know the way.
    You're having a conversation with someone, say at a product launch or a protest march, usually someone you've just been introduced to by someone equally uninteresting, and they mention a colour, or have a particular smell or an anecdote about a holiday or how strawberry jam brings them out in a rash and it's always strawberry that's served in B&Bs and cafés, never raspberry or blackcurrant or whatever, and suddenly my father [*never Dad, never Dad, never Dad*] and his unfixable shadow are there in my head with the whiff of clover [*seriously!*], that dizzy honeysuckle or cool sugary melon waft, yes, and the edge of a bed in a warm and earnest room. Don't know if he's in the bed, or I am, or neither of us. There's a bed and my father and the edge of the bed and clover, in shadow.
    But it's not true, is it? Did I make it up? But he was telling me a story, reading. And.

*[and in the margins she has to ask
if Dad was ill
or was he telling her a story
or did he run away
and is she happy?]*

I used to watch the video of *The Champ* over and over on VHS when I had a VCR. There's one scene that stops me dead, means and says more about the person I know I am than any real or imagined trauma ever will. That scene when the kid says, 'Champ, wake up. Wake up. You can't sleep now. We got to go home.' Or something like that, and the kid cries.
    I'd like to see that video again, and maybe this time the kid does get to go home with the Champ.
    Nine weeks, two days and my baby probably measures 2.5ish cm.

At nine weeks, CRL averages an inch and a half, 2.5ish cm. That's crown to rump length; doesn't include the legs. It seems very improbable. Improbable.

I have a picnic basket of food on the backseat-bed, beside the pile of necessary books and clothes.

[*she met him and somehow*
unmet him. he will
not meet his child. she is not sure
if she will. children die. children
die.]

Before Tom came, saw, conquered and left, I tried to buy a home. Back in the day when we were all trying to be what we were convinced were better selves and they were throwing money at us, I tried to buy a home. Back before the Geiger counter for cash went clickety-fuckety-click.

I had all the bureaucratic, life-atomising bullshit they said they needed: the statements of my financial integrity; vague promises of work on paper; a current annual potentially renewable contract in a science lab devoted to bastardising and analysing food to death; a paper history proving I eventually paid off student loans and was the prudent side of reckless. Bottom line: I look(ed) passably good on paper. The house was textbook (and too big). I had the whole place decorated in my head about a thousand times over (mirrors, mirrors, mirrors, all the better to see yourself with) and filled with gorgeous witty people at dinner parties. There was a room for the coats. Intelligent commuting distance. A septic tank away from the public sewage system and the claustrophobic suburbs and the dying village. It would be in that perfect urban/rural heaven. Water. Water in a pond. Garden. Fish? A lived-in feel. It had, in its previous hominess, held a family or two.

I see my eyes in the rear-view mirror. Gold-flecked. Dark with a preternatural brightness. Tired. Something of a true cat in them today. There is a dove-and-snow seagull walking on the bonnet. He looks at me as if he knows something about me. I watch him from my delicious and eloquent imagination, the part of my mind that isn't dealing with the past.

They didn't give me a mortgage.

Maybe I ought to have made better use of that scrupulous financial advisor. Perhaps I was lucky in the long run, what with the floods, then the wind and the rain rising up and eating fields and streets and houses.

So. No house of my own.

Balzac's Julie fought. He just didn't let her.

[*she is afraid her baby could die*
of cold inside her. she is afraid
she will let this happen.]

How's this story different from anyone else's? How's this crisis of the self unlike the ones untuning men and women all over the country as they go in and out of houses, offices, hospitals, hotels, gyms, surgeries or restaurants?

It isn't.

[*this creature is the only*
possession that binds her to life.
beware of the thraldom of others.
there are paroxysms of thought
at fever heat which can consume
years and years of precious life.]

The wind outside the car is ululating and barking. The fucker is on all fours.

[*honestly, there is grief to come.*
grief is made up of awful regret
and dreariness. it is a terribly sad
soul and a terrible uncertainty
that hangs over death's tomorrow.
but she chose grief.]

My most recent favourite thing to do, in this past week, is to treat myself to a single gin and magic up the slow pleasure of other people's lives. I can really feel that I am back in my past, where the future included a daughter and a man. It's like being between paragraphs, in the place of the unsayable, significant but unable to speak or even to order thoughts. The space inside this car is as big as a cathedral, the boom as deafening with echo.

[*she is not feeling very well. this*
pause is fraught with great
moment. the language of her
eyes completely fills the blank left
by the helplessness of speech.]

It's like being a character I don't understand. [*ha ha.*]

It's like actually being in the 2.5ish cm, being in those litmus, expectant margins, in that field. Lots of things happened in fields. And life is full of misunderstood cryptic remarks.

The father of the collection of cells measuring 2.5ish cm is, of course, Tom. Now, there was a pleasure and it is over and I'm not suggesting, yet, that there may not be such happiness again. I just have marvellous misgivings and the feeling that that part of my life was the rising action and the birth of the baby would be the climax, but I'm not sure.

> [*she cannot tell her story*
> *because she doesn't know it*
> *truly; she misjudged; she*
> *misunderstood; she misheard.*]

Tom. Me and him were a normal curve of things:

perfect milky coffees under a cheap polyester duvet; shared grocery shopping lists; night after night of touching each other in those beautiful dark places;

sweat;

tiny bouquets of weeds tied with little silver chains and rich coloured ribbons as if the metal and velvet could take the weed into a flower;

silent movies;

a steamy kitchen where the yellow buttercup paint curled and peeled like acanthus over the window and the oven cooked one side of a chicken at a time;

walks in damp forests and in scratchy heather where the breeze became a wind very quickly and the hillside took on the aspect of a bruise.

I miss him.

The wind outside the car has reared up on its hind legs, shaking the car as if it needs to be heard. I should be paying more attention. But still, I am still, still in the eye of the coming storm, that is what the vortex of this car is.

I need to pee.

Between the continuing but now media-quiet war in Syria, or whatever that war is—peaceful protest, violent insurgency, civil war, religious war, dastardly proxy war—between that and foetal measurements and doomy global-warming internet porn, there's hardly a minute in the day to deliberate about my own unemployed self. All I do is scratch notes in the margins of poor Julie's life to show I really tried to pay attention in this world. I am becoming marginalia. This makes me laugh.

[how easily we pass by degrees
out of people's lives.
how inevitably forgotten we are.
how the possession of children
is a weak shield against oblivion.
if she was to really see her own
very diluted moral agony,
it would destroy her completely.]

And my favourite food, my absolute favourite food, is oysters, although it's been a while. When it is misty outside the car I sometimes open the windows and breathe in the metal and smoke air, my mind emptying itself of everything except the ceaseless burden of sorrow that constantly hums. It makes me deaf. I cannot hear happiness or hope. The squalor and leafy faith of the city murmurs and grunts far away over the galleries, awkward architecture, bald-headed estates, and I walk the city on Google Earth. I'm homeless. And it happened suddenly. No one plans this.

It was on a Tuesday night. Tom came to me with a choice that he had made.

This story doesn't have a proper ending.

There is no twist.

[insert twist]

I was wandering through the aisles in Aldi—thinking *isles* in Aldi like I could be snorkelling in turquoise-composed waters somewhere in the Aegean instead of between gluten-free cornflakes and Fairtrade teabags—and I was watching the people scowling at their kids, the slow motion of despair in the way they filled their baskets, and I had to fight to crush the impulse to take the melons and the soul-destroying star fruit and squish and squash and pulp them cruelly into the floor as if I was certain of what I was doing. I didn't. I didn't because I didn't want all those people to have to protectively gather their children. I was reading them and their needs.

[she is really, really close
to the edge. almost close enough
to fall or be heard...]

Think about this: Julie's friends often found her absorbed in prolonged musings; the less clairvoyant among them would jestingly ask her what she was thinking about, as if a young wife would think of nothing but frivolity, as if there were not almost always a depth of seriousness in a mother's thoughts. Unhappiness, like great happiness, induces dreaming. I dream of dead men and anger and people dying of pain. I made choices to get here. To be in this place. I did. Shame. Shame. Shame.

Before the boom went boom, until recently actually, while I was still working at the food lab, and where, at break times and between swabs and shelf-life analysis, we watched videos of ISIS fighters getting whacked or whatever, developing our politics from 11 o'clock trawling. I'm gone beyond argument on that front. I mean (and I must include myself), we are at desktops, itchy fingered, liking, approving, looking for approval, applauding ourselves for how we turn out in outrage and small donation after the disaster, open our pockets for a blink, wow, look how caring we are! My arse.

In this multi-windowed room of the car, condensation makes my breath, my unsaid, compose a shield against the outside briskness. On the flimsy shields of this befogged womb I want to draw kind, smiley faces to watch me think, weepy finger lines with the gist of a future in them.

The disturbed gale outside has left any haphazardness it had behind, and is full of intent. I miss all the enumeration and allergens, the pesticides, additives, E-numbers, all the micro universes, the hybridised fluorophores. I miss the safe language of the lab. Julie couldn't know this.

Tom and I. It was easy. There were no demands. Tom with his curly hair and comfortable laughter.

[*but she will ask herself*
is he really gone. mistrust, doubt
and the tyranny of hope bloom,
create a fog, a doom.]

Tuesday.
    Almost ten weeks ago.
    'I'm dying.'
    'Yeah,' I laughed.
    'It's serious.'
    'What?'
    'I want to die alone.'
    'What?'

'Stage 4. You need to leave. I'm really sorry.'

'Tom?'

'I'll give you a couple of days to pack.'

'Fuck.'

'I'm really sorry.'

'Are you really dying?'

'Yes. And I'm going to do it alone and I don't want to talk about it. I understand that this isn't easy but I have made my decision.' He stared into my face. A very faraway language. I only ever touched him once more.

I couldn't find anything in his words except words.

I couldn't find anything in his eyes except colour.

I couldn't find anything in the room except fear.

'When?' I reached out to touch him and he flinched.

> [*sometimes, a whole tragedy*
> *grows out of a single gesture;*
> *the tone in which a few words are*
> *spoken can rend a life*
> *irreparably in two*
> *and she never stands up*
> *and screams.*]

But he didn't answer the 'when' I meant.

'Well, you have to move out this week. I've booked a hotel for you for a month. That should give you time to find a place. I'll leave you here for the week to get your stuff sorted. I'll pay for storage.'

He didn't smile. He didn't cry. He didn't grimace or shout or whisper or falter.

I found a sentence, or most of one.

'We were in that fucking bed having sex last night and saying how much we loved each other and you… you…' I hit him. I hit him. An angry touch across his face.

He didn't smile. He didn't cry. He didn't grimace or shout or whisper or falter.

And another group of words.

'How could you? How could you? You knew. You fucking knew.' I said. 'Is it fucking true? Is it?'

The last words Tom said to me in that new impossible-to-find-anything-in voice were, 'Thanks. Goodbye.' He was wearing a blue jumper that I hadn't seen before.

There is no place in a story for an event like that. There is no formula. There is no way to present the structure of it, all of its unknowns, or the moments and minutes that it covers and uncovers. The hours and weeks that it exposes.

Tuesday night though, that was the beginning.

Yes.

I have father issues.

Ages ago I made a will. There is a methodical practical side to me. If I put myself on paper I am real in this world. I have a purse full of memberships, various levels of club cards, a really good track record in petitions, and I just love the chuggers. I love to meet them on the streets, watch their disinterested performances. They have a way with the body in space that makes me want to hug myself. Tom used to get patiently annoyed at the time it would take us to go across town. I'll sign anything for the future, to stop animals dying, starvation among humans, forests vanishing; add my voice to the throng of the needy wanting puppet dictators unmasked; be indignant at gangs pointing missiles or using planes for secret bad stuff.

But I draw the line at images of mutilated foetuses and representations of the divine.

I used to make inter-library loan requests for books I wanted to be seen holding.

And in case I do never have a future, all my earthly belongings at that time will go to my sister.

I have a sister. She doesn't know me very well and it's not her fault. She had an odd way with grief. Not a talking way. She sings. More of a hummer really. I think it stops her letting the various parental leavings into her head. I see her every now and again. She doesn't know about the current homelessness or about the baby. Our unknowing chat usually goes:

'You're looking well.'

'That colour suits you. You always had the luck of Mam's skin.'

'How are the boys?'

'Great. Exams and whatnot.'

Then she looks embarrassed.

We ignore the embarrassment.

And, every time we meet, we drink tea.

So I didn't tell her about the shock. The time it must have taken. The secret planning. About what Tom must have known and done. All alone. The visits to consultants. The medical records. The paperwork. The time. The opinions and second opinions but not my opinion. The procedures. The time he smiled at me and now it's not true. The time. The procedures. The time. The assessments. That bloody time. I couldn't tell her about the new jumper. That last shag, the awful simplicity of it. The selfishness.

> [*the self-determinedly pigheaded
> asshole time-stealing arrogant
> fuckheaded loneliness of it all.
> she cannot enumerate the hate.*]

I have one friend too. From college days, although we have gone our separate ways. He's not around very often, especially since the beginning of Tom.

> [*a glance into indifferent eyes
> is the deathblow
> of the gladdest love.*]

Last time I saw my friend, when I dropped my boxes into his attic in the early weeks of Hotel Month (I didn't take Tom up on his offer of storage), his skin was tight with fat and it was slightly blue underneath his fancy clothes. Once, in the days before Tom, my friend came to my suburban estate flat rental for dinner and afterwards I was sweeping the floor and all sorts of things were in my head, but this one memory stands out [*memory of a memory*] of when I saw a boy drown at the beach when I was fifteen.

Before the swim I watched the boy put all his clothes into a Red Devils bag that had a white trim on it and the club badge. His family had a striped wind shelter and matching deck chairs. Mam told my sister and me about the sand, the way it could go soft, and the best thing to do was not to stand up and don't get out of your depth. He was floating like a plastic bag and there was screaming and pointing, men bobbing around and looking stupid. It took them ages to drag him from the waves and all the time I stood on the rocks and once or twice I saw his shut-down face.

I didn't feel like crying. I saw the boy on his back on the sand and he had that awful colour you go. His mother was screaming and his father was real quiet. Just staring. I didn't feel sorry for the boy. People stood around him, praying, as if that could do anything. They forgot about the bag on the rock. I emptied it, took the clothes out and gave them to his father so that he could cover him. I walked away and took the bag with me. And my mother looked at it and she knew who I had taken it from but she never said anything. What I thought about when I watched him drowning was how I would describe the look in his eyes, and how spiritual it all was the way the clouds didn't get in his way.

Perhaps I am drowning inside my car.

[*wow, I have my own water story at last.*]

Yeah.

Homeless.

For three weeks now.

[*childless. loveless. needless.*
homeless. jobless. hungry. gsoh.]

It happened. One day your boyfriend makes a choice, your job goes in the most ordinary of ways, and Wham! you just can't pay the rent because you're not in the hotel anymore and your boyfriend has killed himself in a clinic in Europe and you have no savings and you choose not to ask your sister who doesn't know you and might say no, or your friend who does know you but

[*she should come in from the margins, her I, I, in from the margins.*]

I can't stay with him because I can't tell him I have no place to stay because I can't tell him because I can't tell because I am embarrassed or I don't know myself how to tell the baby that there is no father and I don't understand this tight room I'm in so how can I tell anyone else? I have nowhere to go during the day and I can't understand. No why or way or so easy to, no, can't tell, can't. Can't. Can't.

[...]

No address, no dole. Is it really that simple? No. But it did definitely happen, uncloudy, unimagined.

[*or, it did happen just like that?*]

I wish the security guard would say something.

I think that this is a relatively short period of homelessness. The glibness doesn't mean I think it's okay. It's just not what I want to talk about right now. Perhaps I let it happen because

[shhh, withered heart.
she will not recover from this.
god's fingers are cold, bony
and massively disinterested. they
are pitiless and uncaring. they
exist in grief. a cold look
might kill her.]

hey, I can't go there, or I am swept away, washed off the edge of my life into this room, the pages of this book. I check the wing mirrors for the security guard. I check the prepositional sky for the disappearing sun. I check the battery icon. I read a few pages in the last evening light.

I am thinking a story into existence in the weird silence of the passenger seat.

It's me.

But homeless and me don't go together.

I mean.

I am staying in my car.

It could be worse.

I have a car.

It doesn't go anywhere.

Tom never mentioned the smell. The book's pages are like clothes after a bonfire. I push my face hard into them and inhale noisily because that smell is Tom. Before. I breathe him into me. Like when he was real and honest. The wistful smoke that insists itself into your skin after camping, after happiness. But perhaps this book was rescued from a house fire. Perhaps the smokiness of the breeze on my face when I pull my thumb along these ragged edges, that wood-charred air, is someone speaking to me from the past. The car is impressed with the faint whiff of something burnt. Only thing is. I am not a smoke reader.

I got here (as if I could tell what *here* is) because of the bank manager. Because of Tom and his faithlessness. Because of all of the versions of personal history there are. Because of sex on a Monday night. Because of people walking on and off the stage, people moving from the past into the present. My need because. Womb of my because.

In the past I have been a nest builder. The vulgar, kitsch and unclassifiable spaces I've lived in, the rooms I've shared. Nests. I will make this car a nest until the future time happens. Get a pleasant odour tree. I will feather it. [*I would tell the security guard about the future.*]

And I make memories of myself for my child(ren): Yes, there was the time I saved the boy on the beach and he gave me his Red Devils bag, and way back, that magical time I experimentally lived in a beautiful red Opel Corsa, ha ha ha, and the time I lived in a house that was all hallway, and the time I did a bungee jump and thought it was the hardest thing I would ever do, the time I was wrong about the bungee jump, the time I spilled a hot coffee as I walked the hallway from the kitchen to the sitting room, the times I told them the story of Little Red Riding Hood. And there was the rain. The puddles. The restful fun baths in the daytime. Morning mists blurring the cranes over the hospital? Finger animals on the windscreen?

I wish I knew where he bought that jumper and why. Why did he need a new jumper?

I have a feeling that the damage after this storm will be the sort of thing that ends up in fairy tales in years to come. Or one of my water stories. Tales of warning, of not listening to the forecasters, of choosing to confront the beast. [*waves that greedily pull young boys away, winds that take the very roof off existence.*] The noise of the wind from the inside of a car is interesting. It demands that you listen to it.

Baby has no father. It's not really a conflict or a climax or a rising action.
    I just don't know what to do. It should be written in the margins. I should be.
    Tom goes. I make my own story. My own memories.
    All that missing potential in the background of the future.
    And it's so sad.
    [*this writing in the margins doesn't work, does it. I/she/I cannot hear her/myself/me.*]
    No.
    It's still me in the rear-view mirror. Me.
    [*just me.*] Here.
    On the page.
    I don't smile. I don't cry. I don't grimace or shout or whisper or falter.
    [*once upon a time…*]

Ghosts

.

rain teeming straight
as pine needles
the pause between
you and your prey

.

fuglemyrå
fowl mire
full mouth

.

sognsvann
swansong
soft sung

.

cross / walking
switching / code

.

The letters too make lines, the curve of waves, the cool lines
of a forgotten face, a ghost, once a guest, gone now, now gone

.

David Toms

Rockaway

a stone
in my hand
like a mouse
sliced in half

my calves strain
crossing the sand
the ferry as it
crosses Puget Sound

Tradition bearer

no pen but tongue
no page but air
he sung

David Toms

cuckoo flower

show me someone who weeps at roadside verges
at bursts of daisies and i will show you the inside
   of my wrists   *purple coneflower*   *white ox-eye*

   i am too soft to look at hedgerow strays
froth of cow parsley   *wild poppy*   or to walk
down a motorway at twilight while the sun paints

   warehouses into bruises   *red campion*
blue harebell   is there anything more exquisite
than cars streaming through tunnels?

with closed eyes i am at a beach house
at midnight   *sea campion*   *scurvy-grass*
   but mine are open   *black-eyed susan*

is there anything more exquisite than leaving
without parting words?   yes   the firm tongue
   of courage   *spiked campion*   *creeping thistle*

   show me someone who sobs at dusk light
reflected in tenement windows   tarns
of cloud glass   *cowslip*   *milkweed*

   i will show you the weight of a smile
falls at the same speed as unuttered questions
dame's rocket   *annual honesty*   i am most selfish

when sunsets blush to their edges   i am detached
as   *candytuft*   cloud wisps   *jewel weed*
   touch-me-not   what if i fell with no resistance?

   sweet pea   *sweet violet*   what if a feather
beat me to the ground?   *dog rose*
bleeding heart   *musk mallow*   *bittersweet*

Eloise Hendy

We Are Appalling

Keith Ridgway

Summer passed. It was a staccato year of hot weeks cut up by heavy rain and there was flooding on the news. Nothing much was done about anything, either nationally or around the house. The crisis widened, and the hedge at the end of the field grew to such an extent that it swallowed the bathtub filled with mint, almost overnight. Marianne walked down to look for it and found a dying starling twitching on the grass by the big tree. She insisted it was a starling. Bert thought it might be a sparrow. They spent an hour trying to figure it out on the internet, the now dead bird lying between their laptops and both of them pretending they didn't mind this at all—a little death on their kitchen table. They each left it to the other to get rid of, and later realised that neither had. Pinecone dozed contentedly in his corner amongst a scattering of feathers and debris, and they were horrified. They didn't speak to him for days. In early August another dog turned up at the door after a downpour, his wet smell filling the hall when Marianne let him in. Bert was annoyed, Pinecone furious. But Marianne towelled him dry, fed and watered him, declared that the presence of a collar but the absence of a tag meant that she could keep him and call him Elephant—because of his grey pelt and his lumbering gait. He was some sort of mess of boxer and greyhound and... mule? This was their working theory. When a woman from the village came looking for him the next morning, Marianne lied twice and then gave up. Elephant was taken away, his gait a lot more sprightly on the way out of their lives than it had been on the way in.

It was six hours to London and Bert suspected they had made a mistake. It was not that it was unpleasant. The house was old and draughty and they had spent the first several nights terrified of noises and silence, shadows and doors. But that had settled, and it was comfortable—in a new way of thinking about comfort—and resolutely quiet. No airplanes. No traffic. No people. Marianne was, as she put it, writing her head off. They had set up separate work rooms, and were diligent in keeping out of each other's way, meeting in the kitchen for lunch and dinner, sometimes going for walks together, usually ending up in front of the television in the large front room by eight or nine to argue over what to watch and to share a couple of glasses of wine. All of it was pretty much what they had hoped for. Which left Bert wondering if perhaps their hopes had been a little small, a little sad. And he missed being able to slip out to have casual sex with men. He missed it much more than he had expected. In the city it had become routine. The apps made it easy. Three or four times a week he would go and have sex in a flat somewhere. An hour, maybe two. He had four or five regulars and they messaged him all summer. *Where are you? You're gone for good? Well, let me know if you're in town. Don't be a stranger. Missing… you know what!* The messages were not helpful. But he couldn't block these men, or forget them. He would, after all, be going back to the city. As often as once a month. As soon as he got things sorted work-wise. Meanwhile he was stuck with Marianne in the middle of nowhere, and they were resisting a car. Bert had never learned to drive and while Marianne had, her license had long since lapsed. The apps put him about eight miles from a teenage-looking bare chest and an ageless, mustachioed man who declared more than once that he was *NOT* into *time wasters or hook-ups*, which, it occurred to Bert, ruled out everything. He had walked all over the village and environs in the hope of stumbling into a cruising area. But there had been nothing, except an elderly man who had hailed Bert while ostentatiously pissing in the bushes beside the graveyard. Pinecone had gone for a look, or a sniff, but Bert stuck to his examination of the headstones. All the dead are loved, and all the loved are dead.

He did not confide in Marianne, though he could have, he supposed. They had never had a physical relationship. She was, as Bert understood it, asexual. And he was, as she seemed to understand it, an insatiable idiot. *He likes cocks,* she would tell their friends. *Can you imagine?* She plainly couldn't. Her lack of empathy for really any sort of sexuality struck him as suspicious sometimes, but they'd been through it often and to no avail. She was simply baffled. And baffled that he was baffled. It was as baffling to her, she said, as a love of football or model aeroplanes might be. She did not judge. She just thought it was stupid.

The house sat on eight acres, marked out by walls and fences that needed fixing, and with what used to be—they had been told—a stable, though it seemed to them that it had much more likely been some sort of equipment shed, there being no signs of anything horsey anywhere, while there were piles of wood and metal that seemed like they might have fallen off things. 1910 was the date the estate agents put on the house. Though their cattle-farmer neighbour, Mr Busby, said it was much older—it had just been built on top of, like a church, getting uglier over the years. Marianne liked gruff Mr Busby, a widower, and his three healthy grown-up sons—young men whose photos you might expect to find, she said, on the back of your pack of bacon in Waitrose. Cattle, Bert reminded her. Not pigs. His attitude to them though was just as peculiar: they were friendly and immensely handsome and made Bert feel terribly sad.

Their other neighbour was a mega-farm, hated by the Busbys and the source of much talk in the village. The number of chickens it held was at least 800,000 at any one time, they were told, and would often nudge one million. Marianne and Bert stopped buying chicken for a few weeks but it was such good value, and well, it was local. In July, almost exactly one month after they'd moved in, a man from the mega-farm called with a bottle of wine and a bunch of flowers and apologised for a smell that they hadn't smelled. He was very chatty and polite, and told them that Pinecone was adorable and their (completely overgrown) flower beds a slice of paradise. The next day, in the afternoon, a sudden stench enveloped the house and Bert and Marianne staggered out of their rooms and watched each other sweat and turn pale. It was as if all the piss in the world had soaked into their eight little acres. Ammonia, basically, the Busbys told them, give or take. Better get used to it. The middle son came over in the evening and explained how the wind worked around here—where it went and what it tended to carry, and when to open windows in the east and close them in the west and where it might be good to put out bowls of bicarbonate of soda. Marianne was very grateful. She had a lot of intelligent questions. Bert, on the other hand, followed proceedings as if he might be interrogated later about every movement, every gesture, every glance. The Busby boy, in his T-shirt and shorts and with a chain around his tanned neck, moved like a courteous animal—a stag in a clearing, a horse on a hill. Bert couldn't think of any other animals and stayed as silent as possible and watched. Marianne at one stage had to nudge him out of her way. After the young man had left, Bert drew the curtains in his studio and spent twenty minutes thinking about hills and clearings. He put it out of his mind as soon as he'd finished, but the smell was part of it too. The smell embraced him.

Summer passed. It had gone completely by the second week of September when the bathtub of mint reappeared and two days of cold rain put Pinecone into a depression. A leak developed, from the roof to the landing to what Marianne was calling the library but which was nothing more than a store room for boxes they had yet to unpack. Added to that was the broken window in Bert's studio, the missing step on the wooden stairs to the cellar, a patch of persistent damp in the hall by the front door, the tiles falling off the main bathroom wall, the lack of electricity in the spare bedroom, the warped and unopenable second door to the living room, the broken downstairs toilet, and the overgrown front garden—which neither of them mentioned though they both stared at it in silent despair from separate windows at least a couple of times a day. Marianne eventually, tentatively, suggested that they simply pull everything up. No plants. No bushes. No flowers. Leave the grass and the empty beds and the hedge at the front. Rake the gravel driveway. Make it *minimal*. They could, she said, find some interesting bits of wood or metal in the stables and paint them. A sculpture garden. Bert declared it a fantastic idea. He was so enthusiastic that Marianne had second thoughts. They were, she said, too lazy. They had no practical skills. They should do some courses. Bert gave a semi-serious little speech about them being *workers in song*, something which came as much of a surprise to him as it did to Marianne, who was nevertheless moved. They agreed on the plan. Then they kept putting it off.

There was a new prime minister. Marianne shouted at him on the television and spent an evening trying to decide whether to join the Labour Party or the Lib Dems. Bert refused to have an opinion one way or the other, and Marianne shouted at him about Nazis for some reason, and then apologised, saying that the crisis was distorting the national psyche and turning all of them into *buckets of unmanageable emotion* who *sloshed around* and *leaked*. She revealed that she was working on a *very political novel*. It would shock him, she said. It would shock him and all of her readers. Bert felt that he was close to being all of her readers lately, and also felt that he was unshockable as far as her books went, but said nothing. She joined the Lib Dems and calmed down. Bert quite liked the new prime minister, but could never admit to it.

He was managing his appetites a little better, he thought. Masturbation bookended his day and seemed to keep him relatively sane, if slightly embarrassed. He dreamed of London. He dreamed of all its men. But he had no real reason to go, and was afraid that if he made one up the deceit would become a habit. They did not deceive one another. For eighteen years they had lived honestly and in love, and he thought sometimes that it was the greatest achievement of their lives—better than any of Marianne's odd books, and certainly better than any of his distinctly pedestrian music. They had wanted to write operas together, and they had not. But they had written some quite nice songs, and they were happy. Weren't they? He stopped working one morning and sat up and then stood, and went urgently to Marianne's study and knocked at the door. She opened it only because she thought something must be wrong. Why on earth else would he disturb her? He told her he loved her. He said it had seemed suddenly very important that he tell her that. She opened her mouth, and then closed it. Frowned and then smiled. To watch her was a joy, and all that he felt reassured him that this was not an act, and he realised that it had in fact been a test—telling her this, in the middle of the morning—it had been a test of whether it was still true. And it was. She hugged him and they kissed and went for a long walk around their domain, hand in hand. On the way back Marianne found another dead bird.

There were further bad smelling days. Not many. But they disturbed Bert in ways that he could not properly identify. The man from the mega-farm called again, and a third time, delivering more wine, and chocolates, but no more flowers. He said the smell was an ancient one, associated with chicken farms since chickens were first farmed, and that it was in *The Canterbury Tales*. And, he said, just they wait until the Busbys did some muck-spreading, which they would as winter eased up, and then they would have the whole rich aroma of the land around them, *in stereo*, he laughed. They asked him not to come back. He left his card and two bottles of champagne. Bert researched muck-spreading on the internet and made himself anxious again. He would go to London. He would go for a weekend and to hell with it. He told Marianne his agent wanted to see him, and that he had a meeting at the BBC about a couple of possible commissions, and that he needed to go shopping for various pieces of equipment and a new mandolin. All of this had some basis in fact. His agent was always happy to see him. The BBC were commissioning. He needed a mandolin. But it was cobbled together in such a stupid way that he felt depressed about it and may even have changed his mind had Marianne not expressed immediate enthusiasm for the opportunity to invite her niece for a few days. Lisa was twenty-two and a poet and insufferable to Bert.

He booked a room in a terrible place in London Bridge that overlooked nothing. He had earplugs but it was silent as a tomb. He had made contact with his regulars and lined up three dates, two at their places, one at the hotel. He had a quick and dispiriting lunch with his agent in a Pret A Manger in Holborn and walked back, sweating across the river in an unseasonable heat. He called Marianne to make sure that Lisa had arrived and that they were both okay. Of course they were. Lisa was exploring the house and finding it *spooky* and *cute*, but was quiet, a little distant and strange, Marianne said. She suspected some nonsense to do with a man.

Bert showered and felt awkward. He had friends he could call. But they would want to see him and he wanted to have sex. He found himself watching the news in a sort of liminal soup of anticipation and impatience. Then his date for the evening cancelled on him. Furious, he spent an hour on the apps but he was too agitated to be able to bear any sort of human company now, and he gave up. He ate a pub burger and had to have another shower, and thought that maybe it was just the city he missed, not the sex at all, and that he should go on a big long walk. He lay down to think about it and fell asleep. He woke briefly at 4AM to a terrifying disorientation that spun him into panic until he remembered that he was a human being in the age of human beings, and that he was known and loved, though he was temporarily alone in a city that no longer seemed to care that he existed.

He had sex twice the next day. Once by arrangement, in his hotel room, which was all very friendly and civilised and bore no relation at all to what he had thought he wanted. And then again later with a new man from one of the apps who invited him to a riverside flat that had a baby grand piano in it that the man couldn't play. He said it just came with the apartment, *like all the furniture*. He was French, and seemed amused at Bert's stricken expression. He was in London just for a while, overseeing crisis preparation for a small chain of coffee shops and a large chain of fast-food outlets, for his clients who owned both. His clients were a private equity group behind *a very big* chain of coffee shops in France, as well as a chain of airport restaurants, a chain of bars in South Africa and a chain of fast-food outlets in India. He stripped as he listed them. Bert, exasperated, sucked him off as quick as he could and left, breaking free—he found himself thinking—of the chains. He ate in a crowded pizza place and tried to get drunk on their wine but couldn't. Back at the hotel he was looking up train times to see if it was possible to check out early and just go... home, he supposed. But then something stupid happened.

There had been another arrangement, to visit a man in Bermondsey who he had met before, and who sometimes had a friend with him. While he hadn't exactly forgotten about this arrangement, Bert had been refusing to recall it. It was for 8PM. Just after, the man sent him a text. *Hey sexy, are you on your way?* Bert had to decide and he could not decide. There was a knock at his door. He rose to answer it, and at the same moment the phone in his hand began to vibrate. His date was calling him. He opened the door and simultaneously, without quite being in control of or understanding his actions, he answered the phone.

—Hello?

In front of him was a middle-aged woman who seemed to sway. She regarded him with astonishment.

—Who are you?

—Albert! Where are you?

—What?

—Are you coming?

—Who the crap are you I said.

—Hello?

—I think you have the wrong room.

—What?

—Do I? Do I? The wrong room is it?

—Jesus. Are you all right?

—This isn't my

—Yes I'm fine.

—Oh do I? Oh crap.

—What's going on?

—Uh

—I'm sorry mate. What an idiot. I'm... is this the fifth floor?

—Should I ring...

—Sixth.

—You're not on your way then.

—I was just about

—Ring

—What?

—Sorry. I was

—No no, I want

—No no what?

—Ring ring

—You want what?

—Is it too late?

—Depends

—No not you

—What?

—Hold on

—Jesus

—You alone?

He took the phone away from his ear.

—I'm sorry. You have the wrong room. Crossed wires... purposes. Goodnight.

He closed the door. There was a hooted *ha* from the other side, and what sounded like a kick. He raised the phone.

—Christ. I'm sorry. Listen it'll take me twenty minutes to get to you. That okay?

There was silence. He'd hung up. Bert sat on the bed. There was another kick at the door. He bounded over and jerked it open ready to say something he would regret, but there was no one there. He scowled, furious, and went back inside and tried to slam the door but there was something in it that resisted slamming and it jammed and he found that it could only be closed with minimal force so that it would not slam, and he wondered if it was broken, but then realised that it was by design, and thought that this was actually quite clever, and a good feature to have in a hotel, and also worried briefly if it was not somehow a fire risk though he couldn't, just at the moment, think how, and at the same time he hated it and hated every thought and tendency and person that had been involved in coming up with and creating something which so deviously frustrated the absolutely boiling, hideous rage with which he was now suddenly and completely overcome. The door closed gently with a supercilious *thwunk*, and Bert burst into tears. They had sold their house. Their home. They had sold their home in Peckham and bought an eight-acre mess in the middle of nowhere and he was homesick for God's sake, homesick for a home they had thrown away for some barely articulated idea that involved better air, less noise, fewer people, cost of living, peace and quiet, love, safety, England. Bert lay on his side and let it all out. Was it a test? Was that what it was? Let's cut ourselves off and see if we are enough for each other? My God they could have just rented a place in the highlands for a few months. They could have done a summer swap with a couple in Stockholm, the Ardennes, Guatemala. He was muddled now, his face wet, forlorn and lonely and stupid. Why had he not stayed with friends instead of sneaking into the city like an idiot thief? Why had he not been honest with Marianne? Why was he filled with guilt and shame and fury? He hated his entire self, and a fire raged through him for fifteen minutes, leaving him thoughtless and exhausted and as bitter as a baby. As he fell into a wounded sleep he dimly realised that he had forgotten completely about the mandolin.

Summer had not passed. He rose early and checked out of the hotel and walked through the hot morning to a Sunday timetable of slow, sweaty trains that brought him eventually, in late afternoon, to the village, where he took a taxi. He had sent a couple of texts to Marianne but she had not replied, which meant either that she was working, or that Lisa was still there. He'd also texted the man he'd stood up the night before, apologising. He got a confusing reply saying it was good to hear from *Albert* after so long, and he didn't know what he meant about last night, and that it would be nice to see him again. The man had either mixed him up with someone else or was being sarcastic in a way Bert didn't understand. In any case, it eased his sense of shame. The taxi driver complained that the smell was back. That it had been in the air all day. Bert didn't get it until he was walking up the drive. He didn't think it was as bad as before but it also seemed slightly different—a little less pissy, a little more mouldy. He had done a lot of thinking. He had made decisions.

Marianne was in the kitchen staring at a tea towel. It was an ordinary white tea towel with squares of red hatching, hanging from a hook beside the window above the sink. Usually a little bell on a yellow ribbon hung there. But now there was a tea towel, and Marianne was staring at it, her head slightly cocked. She had not responded to his calls nor had she turned to face him as he'd come in. Her arms were by her side. The smell was worse inside the house than outside and Bert's resolve faltered a little. He asked her whether she was all right. No answer. He walked over to her. Her shoulders were slumped, and there was a tremor in her hair. He thought for an awful moment that she'd had a stroke. But when he walked in front of her her eyes snapped onto his and she straightened up.

—Oh. I didn't hear you come in. I was looking at this. It moved. It's been moving. I'm absolutely certain. The towel, I mean. Can you see it moving? Well I think it's stopped now but my God, Bert, it moved like a sort of terrible puppet, like those awful things on the television in the cold war, do you remember those terrifying children's shows that there used to be from behind the Iron Curtain? Well that's the first thing I thought of, though I really don't know why, because I can't really pin it down, it just moved, danced almost, like a glove puppet—that's it, as if there was, as if underneath it there was...

—Darling, darling. Come here. You're rattled. Come here, love. That's it. It's okay. It's just a tea towel. I'm home now. It's all right.

—You forgot the mandolin, she said.

He was hugging her, his eyes looking for Pinecone and not finding him, and it took half a second for him to realise what she'd said.

—How did you know?

—I don't know. So you did?

—Yes. Completely.

—Were you having sex?

—Yes, a little. But it made me very depressed and I missed you very badly and I want to do everything properly from now on. I want to be here properly, not just half here. Not just hovering. Properly be here. I love you very much. Where is Pinecone?

—Lisa took him.

—Took him where?

—To see the chickens.

—Darling.

He detached himself from her embrace and moved back to see her face, his hands on her shoulders. She wasn't looking at him. Her eyes were fixed on the tea towel.

—You're not making much sense.

—No. I know.

—Are you all right?

—I am very frightened.

—Of what?

She nodded at the tea towel.

He turned and looked at it. It was still. And then it moved. Almost imperceptibly at first, it moved upwards, still holding its coned shape—as if the hook that held it was moving too. But then the two bottom corners travelled upwards as well, at a faster pace, making the whole thing wider, and then the towel seemed to flatten out horizontally for an instant and behind it there seemed to be… it fell again, and swayed back and forth a few times. Bert thought: *How is she doing that?* But she was behind him now, holding his arms, and he could feel her body against his and she was doing nothing other than shivering as if cold.

—There's a draught.

—No.

She was right. The day was completely still. The windows closed. The doors. It had stopped. It hung there, still, a little damp and dirty looking. Was it theirs? He didn't know. He found that Marianne was gripping his arms far too tightly and he hadn't noticed, and now that he had it seemed risky to tell her to stop. He touched her hands. She let go. He took a step towards it. Immediately it flew from the wall towards him as if thrown. Marianne screamed. Bert ducked or dodged low and it landed on his shoulder and he hit his head on the side of the kitchen counter, and he shook and brushed the thing off him, flailed it off him, got it somehow *off* him. It fell to the floor and lay there. His head was sore and a ringing filled his ears. They looked at each other, and at the towel. Then Bert followed Marianne's gaze to the wall. On the hook by the window was a furiously shaking bell on a trembling yellow ribbon. Bert and Marianne screamed together and moved as one to the door, their arms trying to gather all the parts of each other and ensure nothing was dropped, each travelling the same way and looking backwards at the impossible little bell dancing and ringing in the air as if shaken by a hand, but of course there was no hand. In the hall Bert tripped over his own bag and banged his head again. Marianne sat on the floor beside him and they clung to each other as if atop a burning tree.

Eventually the ringing stopped. They stayed on the floor, and after a while the silence was as disconcerting as the noise had been, and they scuttled backwards towards the front door. Bert's head was bleeding, and Marianne spent a minute asking him in whispers to count backwards from ten and who the prime minister was, and he counted forwards from ten and said Tony Blair but she didn't notice. He said he was fine, but he felt sick and dizzy. He couldn't get the tea towel out of his mind. It had touched him. It was disgusting. The sense of disgust was very powerful, though the thing had not felt like anything other than a tea towel thrown over his shoulder. It had not seemed to move while on him, and it had not left anything behind when he got it off. He glanced to check. Marianne was still trembling. There was silence. The smell seemed to have gone, or changed, or perhaps they were used to it now. He suggested that they call a taxi and go find a hotel somewhere and come back first thing in the morning, perhaps with a Busby or two, and investigate in daylight, when they were less…

There was a knock at the door.

Well. Look at them, sitting on the floor dishevelled and scared, like two children frightened of the dark, of shadows, of tea towels and little bells. Bert felt ridiculous. He stood up gingerly, telling Marianne they were being silly, and he held a hand out to her and she grasped it and he pulled and they stood clinging gently to each other and looked at the big black door. Silence. Bert called out:

—Hello?

… and Marianne jumped, and the silence resumed.

He stepped up to the door and laid his ear against it and could hear nothing at all.

—Hello?

He looked at Marianne.

—Where is Lisa?

—She went for a walk, to see the chicken farm. She was furious about it. She was furious all the time. She isn't back. It's her. It must be her.

—Lisa?

Another knock and they both jumped, a little backwards, a little down, but Bert felt braver now and he took a boxing stance and grabbed the latch and turned it and pulled the door open. There was no one there. No one. Nothing. Nothing there. The steps. The gravel. The driveway. An empty English evening, timid against the heavens. Nothing.

—You should call her. Call Lisa.

Marianne had left her phone in the kitchen. Bert's was in his pocket, but he didn't have Lisa's number. So they stood in the hall inside the open doorway of their own home and Marianne used Bert's phone to call her sister—not the one who was Lisa's mother, but another one whose number Bert did have—and asked her for Lisa's number, and then of course they couldn't find anything to write with, and did not feel up to memorising, and Marianne asked her sister just to text it, text it for God's sake, to Bert's phone, which she did, and Marianne hung up on her and her questions.

Look at them there. In the open doorway of their home in the country in the evening. Standing together as if about to welcome guests.

Lisa answered almost immediately. Bert listened in.

—Hi M, how are you?

—Lisa, where are you, darling?

—Uh, I'm at a friend's?

—But where? You're in London?

—Yes. What's wrong?

—Lisa, love, why didn't you tell me you were leaving? I didn't know what had happened to you. Did you come back to the house at all?

There was a pause.

—Marianne, I don't know what you're talking about. I'm in London. I've been here all... I haven't been anywhere. Do you mean your house?

—What? Yes.

—Marianne, I've never been to your house.

They stood for a moment holding on to each other and then let go. Lisa's voice continued briefly, but Marianne dropped her arm to her side and then either hung up or was cut off. They looked at each other in silence. Bert had never experienced such silence.

—I am me, he said. But he could not hear himself.

Marianne turned as if to leave the house, but the door was closed in her face, in silence. She moved away from Bert and he watched her as she went past him and stopped. She was looking at the door to the kitchen, which had opened. Bert slapped his ear. Nothing. The smell rushed back—an overwhelming stench—and he clasped his nose and mouth and coughed but made no sound. Then, as if to mark some happy, small event or the passing of a certain time, the little bell began again to ring—clear and loud and joyful.

All the dead are loved. And all the loved are dead.

Chameleon

I am the Lizard Queen!
—Lisa Simpson

In bed last night
with my real self I lay chillin.

Opal vein mined
from no dark Andamooka hunk.

The price of rainbow
is the body's shell, split.

Adaptation no more, bitch.
Out she comes

like the lizard men
sheddin their humanskin.

Carved in luminous
like the fine jade bra

that stunned
when he tore her open.

Trees makin a cathedral
of absence

neon signs like green moons
in their aisles.

Welcome was
the knife in her back

on the steps to Montmartre
cos a long road is life

without ever becomin
the creach that is nothin

& everthin. Like glass.
Like the lobster

translucent as ice
fisherboy netted in Maine.

Little goddess, tidewitch
he returned to the waves.

Because she female.
Because she strange. Rare

as blue amber
seadaughter shadowself
eggcarrier

Róisín Kelly

The Celestial Realm

Molly Hennigan

The first month or so of each stint in the psych ward was punctuated by daily material and immaterial requests, as well as the usual messages from On High. *Clarins Doux Peel. LoUis Armstrng Wat a wunderful World. You are a Duality!… composed of two parts!… what you 'are' cannot be diminished!… and nothing could make up for what you're 'not'!* The material requests were for comfort—to make my grandmother's bed in her basement ward feel like a home. The immaterial requests were songs that God would've sung to her that day or the night before. Phil would want to know all the lyrics, the better to steep herself in his love through the voices of Petula Clarke, John McCormack, Etta James, Rihanna or Luke Kelly. The remaining messages were streams of consciousness flowing from him to her and on through the spiritual magic of unlimited data to my mother and me. Playing the songs for her on Youtube while she lay in her bed reacting was love in action. It was unorthodox love but what Phil marvelled at I did, too, in my own way. She marvelled at God. He loved her. She told me they were like eighteen-year-old lovers. She giggled at the ceiling of her ward when He said intimate things. She couldn't get over how intelligent He was. He would say really smart things, she said. She would repeat them. They *were* smart.

Julia Kristeva says that it is possible to overcome or 'curb' mourning in a way that gives one 'a subliminatory hold over the lost Thing.' She explores this possibility through the idea of prosody: 'The language beyond language that inserts into the sign the rhythm and alliterations of semiotic processes.'

In her intonation and lilt, when singing and also speaking, Phil stresses and rhythmically implies power and loss, mourning and epiphany, all at once. The heights and depths of ethereal meaning for her drag and surge her vocal chords, sharing with me through sound a taste of the pain and beauty she feels. She has been consistently manic and high for some time now but the framework of a single song seems to act as a microcosm of what bipolar disorder has been for her over the years. In just a couple of minutes, pure elation drops to despair.

Lying back in her hospital bed her eyes light up, ecstatic, and she sings, 'Enchanted by her beauty rare I gazed in pure delight [*Her eyes are glinting. She is giddy.*] till round an angle of the road she vanished from my sight [*She waves her hot, swollen hand.*] but ever since I sighing say as I that scene recall, the grace of God about you and your auld plaid shawl. I'll seek her all through Galway and I'll seek her all through Clare—this is the bit He's after singing to me now—I will seek her all through Galway and seek her—[*She pauses. Her lip drops and her face seems heavy with a confused sadness. She wrinkles her nose up and whispers through tears to God.*] Wait, I'm not ready—seek her all through Clare [*She sings nervously now. She seems uncomfortable—her voice disappears with crying as she mouths the words.*] I'll search for tale or tiding of my traveller everywhere. [*She's crying heavily now.*] For peace of mind I'll never find [*Rubbing her tummy and crying.*] until my own I call [*Pauses, mouth bunched, then moves quickly through the next bit in tears.*] that little Irish cailín in her auld plaid shawl. [*Sniffles, takes a deep breath and continues crying quietly.*] Stop. [*She whispers to herself or to Him—I'm not sure.*] Stop! [*Holding both hands together tight, rubbing each other.*] So He's got me now.'

There's a dizziness to the whole thing. It is other-worldly. She comes back to the room. 'So He's got me now,' she says, looking at me with the saddest eyes. She has the weight of different worlds on her shoulders. It is real for her and she is trying to exist in two spaces. To migrate from one universe to another measuring their relative loneliness and judging where best to set up camp. It looks agonising.

Alongside the physical pain of Phil's recurring kidney infections—then her frequent falls; then her breast cancer and mastectomy—is a lucidity that is new. I often wonder if the physical pain of her mid-eighties is a disc pressing on the nerve of her lucidity, releasing the part of her brain that will engage with the truth of her reality. I feel guilty even saying that. *Truth of her reality.* I have been complicit in layering fiction over truth for her, veiling reality. To be a patient in a psychiatric ward is like dying. You are stripped of autonomy while any sense of self is bleached and sterilised—you begin to question what your 'autonomy' even is, or what you would want if you had it. Would you want to leave? Why would you leave everything you know? Patterns you have been forcibly bent to fit into. There is nothing out there that you know. You have either forgotten all of the amazing foods you used to cook, or you don't see yourself as the same person who used to cook them. Days drag into a blind repetition of habits and compliances. You will be rewarded at meal times for engaging. Rewards will vary from a smile to a verbal congratulations but even in the dopiest throes of lithium-induced stupor you will know in your slurred response that these rewards are not sincere. These people are not sincere. Individually, some are. But they are feeding into a system that is designed to control and subjugate you. You are an inmate. You know this. Your family who visit know this but they distract themselves and you from that truth by bringing you fresh fruit and dressing gowns and chocolates and you feed again into their self-absorbed need to feel helpful, to feel righteous. You thank them for the things they bring and the time they give. They don't go home feeling better. There is no lack of sincerity there but now as you lie in a ward in Tallaght Hospital having 'possibly'—they say—fallen out of your bed in the lockdown psychiatric unit in which you live there is nothing sincere about family having visited you there and brought things you like to eat and to wear.

Phil is eighty-five. She has been dying for forty years. She has been revived at times, spending stints in her own home and has even been well enough to take me out for drives in her red Mini. When I was a young child, we mostly went swimming together. I would stand beside her, no taller than her bare hip bone, and watch her put on two tight swimming hats to protect her hair from the chlorine. She looked like a model. Sometimes she also swam with a snorkel and paid no attention to me, mortified and bobbing in the far corner of the pool. Afterwards she would feed me cheese sandwiches on homemade brown bread that was so stodgy it stuck to the roof of my mouth. I once caught a glimpse of myself in the glass cabinet that had the expensive swimming togs and hats in it as I tried to tease the bread down with my tongue and the vein-laced rib on the bottom of my tongue matched my bloodshot eyes.

For the most part, though, she was dying. Slowly. In truth, she was never really in her house in the last few years and, any time she was there, food just stacked up in the kitchen and rotted while she posted sticky notes all around the house for God. And for Satan, sometimes, who for a spell took the form of her neighbours' two-year-old boy. Despite this, she was happy.

*

Phil doesn't like physical affection. She doesn't love you because you don't exist. You are a projection of something. She doesn't care if you're sick because she doesn't believe in cancer. She doesn't care if you have something important coming up. A busy week, a daunting appointment, a divorce, because she believes the world is going to end in the morning. Every morning. Unwavering belief. She won't associate with you as family. She doesn't really believe she is anything to anyone bar having acted the part for a higher purpose which she is now fulfilling. You can now be disposed of. She doesn't tell you she loves you. Nobody knows love like her and God. It is just them. She can't be sure that you will be saved. All she knows is that her and God are the Celestial Realm. I might burn tomorrow morning in the fires of hell, she tells me, as I bring her two oranges from the bag of oranges I have in the car because she won't let me bring her in a full bag of oranges because she won't need that many because the world is ending in the morning.

'Okay,' I say, as I peel an orange. Something instinctively maternal and also naïve in my mother takes offence to this.

'Well, why, Phil? Why won't she be saved?' My mother is in no way religious, but she seems to have been sucked into the narrative.

I frown over at her. 'It's grand.'

'No, it's not. Why are my daughters going to burn in the fires of hell, Phil?'

'I'm not saying they will, Deirdre, I'm just saying they might. It's nothing to do with me.'

'It is. They're your granddaughters'

'Haha, no they're not.' I find myself almost laughing with Phil.

'Mam, it's grand. Thank you though.'

'C'mon, Molly. I need to go. I have to get out of here. We're going, come on.'

That would happen regularly. Phil would unintentionally wind my mam up and she would be wound tight.

*

A few months ago, she began touching her forehead against ours as we were leaving at the end of visits. I couldn't remember the last time she touched me before that. My mam and I both welled up a little the first time, waiting in the corridor that one nurse locked us into before a nurse at the other end of the corridor could let us out. This emotional vacuum. If we brought that emotion out into the car and onto the M50 and into my mam's new apartment it would ruin everything. It would ruin that evening. It would make it impossible for me to go home the next morning and leave her there, alone. I had a sickly shiver and a damp, now cooling feeling under my armpits. It was stress sweat. Particularly sour. Period sweat is pretty disgusting and pungent and sex sweat is quite nice and musky but stress sweat is just bitter. That's the one that will ruin your clothes. I had no appetite and felt a bit dizzy but suggested we get fish and chips on the way home.

'Oh yeah, lovely, what time is it? I think there's two Emmerdales on tonight.'

'Aw deadly.' I wasn't being sarcastic but there was a pause.

We both know I don't watch soaps anymore and I think that carries some layered meaning for my mother. It creates some heavy distance between us which might sound trivial but feels sad. It was all I wanted to do that evening though.

'That'll be nice,' I follow up.

It's still a bit lacklustre. I ask about a character I remember, a child when I last saw the show. She is now pregnant and runs a business. I don't know if I'm more sad that it has been that long since I've spent some quality time with my mother, or that the measure of it is a fictional soap character growing up.

*

I was born on Saint Brigid's Day and people always ask why I wasn't called Brigid. I always liked that my birthday was February 1st for this reason and also because it was the start of spring. I still like it for these reasons. But as a child or even teenager these things didn't mean much. They were just conversation pieces. Saint Brigid wasn't really celebrated enough for me to find much meaning in sharing my birthday with her day, and a new season went unnoticed when I was just shipped back and forth in the same school buses and cars to the same places year round. I knew it was dark when I went to school and dark again when I came out for a few months but I didn't actually care. The warm entrapment of childhood numbed me to the elements since the house I came home to already had the lights on. And, if it didn't, a taller person was with me and was able to reach for the switch. It never really felt like I came into a dark room as a child.

The psychiatric unit is like that too. All hospitals are, I suppose. Always on. Lights always switched on, heating always going. People always there. Never officially closed. Phil is cooped up in this seasonless, sterile, fluorescent house. The setting sun doesn't poke through the closed blinds in her kitchen, beaming a line across dancing dust particles. Or, rather, it does, but she isn't there to see it. I visit her in the winter and she says I should probably get on the road soon, it must be so late. It is only around five, late afternoon, getting dark. She has no concept of time really, or rather she has an institutionalised concept but not a natural one—it is punctuated and marked by meals she is brought. She has lost her concept of time and light and seasons. So we don't talk about winter or summer or longer or shorter evenings. And so we don't talk about spring being a turning point for that, and it being my birthday, and it being Saint Brigid's Day. And so, somehow, we have never spoken either about the fact that her mother, known as Sissy, was actually called Brigid.

Sissy died in Grangegorman Mental Hospital. Generally, people were committed if they didn't conform or contribute—economically or practically—to society. A society that was still reeling from the effects of the Famine, trying to pack away any loose ends and hide what looked unseemly. A doddery uncle, a pregnant single woman, post-natal depression, anything. Modelling ourselves on the oppressor—put the outcasts in there, and give the rest of us a job cleaning or building it.

In his work, *Irish Insanity 1800-2000*, Damien Brennan discusses the secondary functions of asylums in Ireland. 'These institutions were often the largest provider of local employment within communities,' he says. 'This employment included roles directly related to the care of the insane, such as keeper and nurse but also included roles related to the physical and administrative structure of the asylum such as builders, plumbers, store keepers, book keepers and gardeners.'

My grandmother was twelve when her mam died, her little sister was two. Sissy lived in one of the most notorious asylums in the history of this small country. We had the global lead on psychiatric incarcerations per capita, beating the former Soviet Union even as we were being drained of population after the Famine. 'The population of Ireland almost halved between 1841 and 1911, decreasing from 8,175,124 to 4,390,319,' writes Brennan. 'This is the same period that saw the institutional residency of the 'insane' increase more than seven times, from 3,498 to 24,655.'

The figures are so staggering they say the only reasonable answer would be an epidemic of mental illness. Rather, the epidemic was of mental conformity to the strict and narrow rules defining what was accepted, what was normal. The line was so narrow and unforgiving it wound back upon itself—it became the sickness. People were incarcerated for all types of reasons—sane people who were committed if they were the black sheep of the family; if they had moral standards, financial disagreements, personal views on arranged marriage. All reasonable, sound, and independent thoughts. Sissy had children, was married, fit the aesthetic. However the full range of emotions from anger to love to jealousy were also ripe for manipulation in the process of incarceration so essentially any person experiencing any feeling in any perceived sense of the extreme was fair game. Brennan again: 'Insanity was a vague, changing and all encapsulating concept which could be applied to most social difficulties so as to facilitate and rationalise the admission of a family member to an asylum.'

I don't have much detail about Sissy. She died in a hospital whose records are difficult to attain. Archival work is being done to preserve the rooms full of patients' personal belongings—their handbags make it seem as if they were plucked from the street and committed. This is important work but just speaks to the sheer volume of incarceration and the ease of follow-through upon accusation. Sissy's belongings might be amongst them. There might be something in her bag to soothe a teething baby she thought she was going home to, lipstick, a key to a house she thought she would sleep in that night, or at the very least lie awake in with restless children.

Sissy is a figment of my imagination. I know she existed and she is the reason I am here imagining her, but still, that's all I can do. There's nothing left of her; only the history of her context and us, now. Becoming acquainted with her through a reading of the psychiatric history of Ireland is jarring. Her history and our present moment, clashing in theory but meshing in reality. Her baby is being hurt in the same rooms now. Female lineage in Ireland feels like a wet, mucky, bloody rag to cling to. It is steadfast, durable. It is tangible, the evidence exists, the stains of suffering are there, but there is no information. Whose blood is where?

I have Sissy's long form death certificate. I can run my fingers along the ink of the writing that says she died at Grangegorman Mental Hospital. I can think of the fact that it was written in the building where she died. I can tell from the dated signature that it was written the day after she died. That she died on the 6th of October. The signature, qualification and residence of the informant: Katheryn O'Donnell, inmate, Grangegorman Mental Hospital. Inmate. Incarcerated.

The language of mental healthcare in the late 1800s through to the 1940s was designed to 'quieten the patient'. Procedures as unthinkable as lobotomies and insulin-induced comas were forms of treatment; the desired outcome was silence. The year Sissy died in Grangegorman was the year, according to the *Irish Medical Times*, that lobotomy was introduced there. We talk about silencing Irish women and it is almost always metaphoric, or rather representative of a particular type of non-hearing. We talk about the female Irish writers whose voices we haven't heard, whose books we haven't read, studied or situated appropriately within the canon. We talk about women who were politically active but not remembered justly. Let's also talk about the women's voices that were physically silenced. The women whose ability to communicate was severed by drilling into the skull. Men too, of course. Minorities and vulnerable people who were deemed idiots, lunatics and retards.

The intersection between these barbaric forms of 'treatment' and the Irish habit of incarcerating sane and healthy people into asylums is a monumental historic travesty. Much like the very nature of the procedure, a 'desired outcome of silence' has persisted around this particular nadir in Irish history. Brennan details the various causes and recorded numbers for incarceration as noted in the 1837 Inspectors of Lunatic Asylums Report with 1,639 people incarcerated for moral causes, 2,006 for physical causes, 1,898 for hereditary causes and 4,577 for unknown causes.

There are blocks and pacifiers all around to quieten the voices that try to shed light on historical injustices. Often, we don't even know what the problems are, and so we cannot begin to address them. This is no accident. But we are the offspring of these injustices, and dissociation is one of the most common things Irish people do. 'They' ran the Magdalene laundries, 'they' performed lobotomies, 'they' killed or left people braindead after insulin-induced comas. In Ireland we can say 'they' and 'we' because 'they' are almost always the Church or the colonial oppressor. This social habit of repeated, and sometimes justified, blaming has become a tool in keeping this part of our history submerged. But it is not always someone else's fault. 'They' aren't only the Church or the oppressor when it comes to the asylum system in Ireland; institutionalisation persisted after respective colonial and religious holds began to loosen. 'Rather than reforming and closing these institutions as symbols of an oppressive colonial legacy,' Brennan writes, 'asylums were expanded within the Irish Republic to the extent that Ireland had the highest rate of mental hospital usage internationally.'

We talk about the relationship between state and church in Ireland. We talk about war and oppression and famine; events that changed the fabric of our country, events that trampled the system we had, forcing us to start again. Everything has been broken and has begun again, except our asylum system. It lurks. Cold, towering buildings sleeping over towns and villages where we do driving tests and get X-rays and collect children from school and donate to Dogs Trust. These institutions blend into the skyline of Ireland, and have withstood every national catastrophe we have faced.

*

Phil's condition has deteriorated markedly in recent months. When I visit, I feel guilty about where I am coming from or leaving for. My guilt is tied into how broad my frames of context are and how narrow are hers. She cannot move much in bed or stand up by herself. She cannot answer the door to see it is me, so my visiting borders on intrusion. She might not want to see me just then. Dignity is compromised; wounded in the crossfire between my wide, roaming existence and her walled one, in the crossfire between unsolicited visits and a policing of personal decisions.

A nurse who doesn't work on Phil's ward but who is passing through the corridor offers to buzz me in as I wait at the door. Displaying due diligence, she comes with me to alert a duty nurse that I am on the ward. I see why that is necessary, but she is nonetheless a little rushed and loud. She is speaking at a high volume in the hopes that a nurse will appear from the TV room or nurses' station or someone's ward. She is bordering on shouting—'Phyllis's granddaughter has come to visit. Phyllis's granddaughter is here.' Having my visit announced like it is a rarity makes me feel painfully distant from Phil. A nurse from the ward does arrive; she nods, and everyone disbands. I am left to my own devices.

The door into Phil's room is held open by a chair. I walk in to find her fast asleep, lying on her right side with both hands tucked under her right cheek and just her bare toes being covered by the blanket which is pushed back to the bottom of the bed. She is in a deep sleep and the position of her hands and pillow are squishing her lips to create a resting pucker face. The soft lines that her lips fold into with the pressure of flesh and pillow trick me into thinking she is content. It looks like a peaceful sleep and I let myself believe that. It also stops me from waking her. It would feel unkind. Also, she would only really be coming around when I have to leave, which is cruel. I sit on the chair beside her bed, indecisive. A nurse walks by and I ask him if she slept last night. He says she did, which tempts me to wake her after all. I text my boyfriend to consult. 'Definitely wake her. She'll be annoyed if she misses you!' Sitting on the edge of her bed, I try gently to rouse her. She wakes enough to see it is me and then closes her eyes again. They have given her something to ease her anxiety so she is drowsy. She has had a rough week. She is in and out of sleep and I'm happy she knows I'm there. I rub her back and the warm glow of sun on the back of her navy cardigan is comforting. I rub in concentric circles for maybe six or seven minutes and I feel friction and dizziness in each cell of my hand. I pause to let the tingle subside. Her hair has fallen to the side of her face. The strands lie hardened and dry on her cheek in front of her ear. I slowly warm them and ease them back behind her ear, tucking them into the crevice at her lobe; the crevice that feels soft and comforted by a gentle touch but if poked accidentally releases some kind of sour sensation in the glands of your neck. I am careful.

I stroke through the hair elsewhere on her head that is a little greasier and smoother. The smell of hair and scalp is the most naturally comforting. It is the smell I associate with the aftermath of heavy crying. It is the first thing your senses notice when they finally come round. When the sun shines warm on the pillow and heats the natural oils in your scalp they smell comforting the way the soil turned over in flower beds smells comforting. I breathe deep and keep stroking her hair. Her skin looks grey and she is sad. Sadder than I have ever seen her.

'I am having a lot of trouble at the moment, Molly,' she says while I look down at the side of her cheek rubbing her back again.

'I know.' I don't prompt in any direction but I expect her to continue. She closes her eyes again.

I know she has been asking my mam to save her during recent visits and crying as my mam leaves. I am prepared for that, or so I believe. More truthfully, I am anticipating it but I know I could never be prepared.

'Sorry, I'm so tired. I just keep sleeping. Just need to sleep again.'

'Do sleep,' I say. 'I'll sit here a while longer and then I won't wake you when I leave.'

'They gave me something to calm me down. It feels nice.'

'Good, that's good. Just go with that relaxing feeling while it's here.' She lulls back into a deep sleep, her soft body heaving with deep breathing. A few minutes pass.

She wakes again and needs the toilet. I take her into the bathroom and she wants me to stay. It is a new context for us both. Our identities and their relation to one another are already formed and solid, but they stretch into new territory in this space. I lift her from her wheelchair and sit her onto the toilet bowl. She seems calm and dignified and I feel close to her.

I use her soap which reminds me of her house, and of me as a child. It is masking another smell in her bathroom that suggests diarrhoea and my immediate reaction is concern. I don't know much but I've always had a sense that these small fluctuations in bodily functions can mean more in old age, can be more grave. In recent months smells of bodily fluids have become increasingly associated with care for me and I wonder somewhere in the back of my mind what that means. There is something about this newfound prioritising of the safety and cleanliness of the bodies around me that makes me think I am ready to have a baby. Also the fact that the name Mabel has been sitting at the front of my mind for a full week and even gave me a surge of excitement the other evening at the prospect of calling a little blank face that and telling other people that that was her face's name. It all feels like a slow, inevitable acceptance that I don't want to put language on yet. In conversation at least. The timeframe of it all seems pressured but slow-moving. Like wisdom teeth coming through.

I don't think Phil cares that she won't meet a baby I might have in the future and I don't think of that potential as a life right now anyway. I do find it difficult that I might love someone else as much as her someday. Someone who she won't have met. Someday when she is no longer here for me to love, not as much as I do now. In loving Phil and learning about her mother I feel like the next round of life and death in my family will be the change I resist most. I once asked Phil what it was like to give birth. She answered dismissively: 'It was all water and legs.'

In nothing is tenderness as important as here

I dreamt that I sent you a poem and you replied 'you're an amateur you're gorgeous' and then we swapped sex tapes

except of course I stole mine off the internet and it wasn't a sex tape but a collage full of people

and someone had a finger in someone else's mouth and I was on the train to Dublin I was on the train to somewhere

and there were my siblings all of a blur and we sat down all wearing white Victorian blouses because that's the style

and it's pebble-dashed and it's the solstice and how nice to be young and able to steal a sex tape and how shocked I was

to see you even if it was only in my dream on the way to Dublin or not on the way to Dublin I'm not sure

Manuela Moser

And yet it is all circumstantial

Beyond the boys playing cricket on the sand the sun was suspended in the west

We sit on a pier to watch it set and realise we are facing home, the same sky, the same sinking into the sea

Here, though, I look directly at it and it doesn't stain my eyes

It is a yolk, a penny, pollution

Quietly turning the blue sky shades of pink and green

And really only the clouds catch the colour

And that night I dream a dream of doorways

And he is buying cats and leaving them in my garden

Offering them, one by one in the crook of his arm

There are low ceilings, white walls and yet it is all circumstantial

Are you engaged in agriculture or independent of geographical limitations? he asks

Manuela Moser

77

This leads us back to the idea of transcendence

All of Prague felt like ghosts to me, you say

And so we went to Prague and it was cold and it was beautiful because it was cold and I got used to the feeling

Each morning we threw open the windows to watch the swans on the river while you were sitting on the deck of a beach house somewhere in Maine watching sailboats and drinking tea

Back then my dreams were actually enjoyable

Now I'm thinking about what he said about monotheism, deserts, God as creator/ perfect/ transcendent etc

And sand and mountains and houses on the side of mountains and the bushes that grow there and sun and that barbwire fence

No clouds, no breeze, no water, what I mean is the heat

The heat in the desert that doesn't fall with the sun; that makes the scent of rosemary good up to a heavy point; that burns like sleet when you first feel it and for all time after that

Manuela Moser

Food Shop

Olivia Rosenthall

My mother said, 'I just don't know why it always has to be my children.'

I was standing outside the supermarket and we were talking on the phone. It was cold and I'd been there for a while. I said, 'I should probably go in and buy some dinner now,' and she told me that she really loved me in a voice that was heavy, like something bad was going to happen. I nodded as if she could see me and then said, 'I love you too.'

After I'd hung up and put the phone back in my pocket, I felt empty, as though I'd forgotten to tell her something important.

There weren't many people inside, and I walked down the aisles very slowly, letting my shoes scuff on the floor. Aside from the tinny music playing somewhere above the shelves, it was quiet, and there was something about walking around an empty supermarket that made me feel as though I was in a film. Each movement became exaggerated or suggestive, as though the way I held the basket was a significant detail. At university I'd never used a basket when I went to the supermarket, I'd carried everything instead. For some reason it'd never occurred to me to use one, even when my arms were full. I thought about this as I stopped at a shelf of jarred sauces and rice and began to compare the calorie content between two packets of noodles. The one with the least amount of calories had more grams of fat and I didn't know which one to choose. Sometimes decisions like this filled me with so much dread that I would abandon the idea altogether and get something else, but it was late and I'd been on the phone with my mother for a while, so I chose the packet with the least calories and decided not to think about it anymore.

Recently, I'd told my boyfriend Ryan about the basket thing, that my reason for not using one was because, subconsciously, maybe, I'd felt as though I couldn't. He'd laughed at this, but not unkindly. We were talking in his living room, sitting at opposite ends of the sofa so our feet were touching. The television had flicked to standby and when I paused to take my cup from the coffee table, I'd felt a shift in the way my presence felt in his house, as though talking about these things now made it okay for me to be there, like I wasn't a guest anymore. I'd tried to explain exactly what I'd meant about the basket, but it sounded clumsy and not how I'd imagined it sounding in my head. I said something about it being a personal challenge, some kind of ritual, or a luck thing. What I'd actually meant was that somehow I'd felt as though I wasn't allowed to use one, but I didn't know how to draw this feeling out of myself and put it into words.

I'd had a lot of rituals when I was young. I'd count all the syllables in a single sentence and add up the total in my head. I'd mash up all the food on my plate so there were no lumps or edges. I couldn't sleep until I'd prayed to God at night. When I was a teenager, I counted all the calories in the food I ate and did two-hundred sit-ups in the morning and 200 in the evening. I exercised for an hour every day and ate cereal for breakfast and dinner (no lunch). After the shopping basket conversation, Ryan told me that I punished myself, and I'd said, 'Probably yeah,' because I'd always agreed with whatever anyone had to tell me about myself, even if it was something I didn't like.

I picked up a carton of soya cream in the refrigerated aisle. My mother and brother are both dairy intolerant, and at some point I'd convinced myself that I was dairy intolerant too. I didn't exhibit any of the symptoms of dairy intolerance, of course, but I felt better when I could diagnose myself with a genuine problem, as if giving my anxieties a name made them real. My mother had called me just as I was getting off the train. She'd told me that my younger brother Jacob had not been himself recently. He'd broken up with his girlfriend and hadn't eaten in days, which I'd laughed at because it seemed like I should, even though my brother and I got on quite well.

He was devastated, she'd told me, because his girlfriend had slept with somebody else and he'd found out through a friend, and not her.

'Wait,' I'd said, 'I thought he'd already dumped her?' and my mother had said, 'Yes, yes. I said that, didn't I?'

I could hear her rattling around the kitchen, tugging at the cutlery drawer that was always stuck. I never liked talking to her over the phone when she was busy. She told me about parties and drunk texts and Instagram stories, despite not knowing what Instagram was. I was impressed by how she always seemed able to tell a story as if she'd been there herself, listing the names of friends that neither of us knew. 'And that other boy,' she'd said, 'the one from Jacob's Economics class, I forget his name… ' The line went quiet and I knew she was thinking intensely. 'Oliver, that's the one. Yes, he might've been there too, but I'm not sure. Anyway… '

My mother had a habit of tucking and untucking her hair behind her ears when she got flustered like this, and I'd started to notice myself doing the same thing. Her dairy intolerance was apparently the result of extreme stress, which was why I believed myself to have it as well. I knew that, really, there wasn't anything wrong with me, that it was easier to tell myself that I wasn't allowed certain foods than entertain the idea of eating them. I picked up a bottle of almond milk and read the back, even though I already knew there were 57 calories per every 250ml glass. There are some things you just don't forget.

I didn't eat after my first boyfriend broke up with me when I was eighteen. He was a couple of years ahead of me in school, though I hadn't really known him until the summer before I went to study English Literature in Edinburgh. By the time we were going out we were both studying at different universities, so we only saw each other at the weekends or in the holidays. He wasn't conventionally good-looking; he was the kind of pale you imagined really sick people to be, and he was small and bony. But my attraction to him ran so deeply that sometimes when I looked at him it felt as though my body had no end or beginning. When we were both home, I would go around to the house where he lived with his mother and grandma. We'd stay up late watching YouTube videos whilst drinking old spirits we found at the back of his grandma's drinks cabinet.

I never felt like I *needed* to dress up for these occasions, but I always did. I would buy outfits that I imagined he would like to see me wearing: flowery skirts and blouses, cardigans with elbow patches. I wanted to be a nicer version of myself, and I felt as though wearing something pretty and wholesome would mean that I would somehow become just that. If he told me that he liked a certain top I'd worn, I would wear it over and over. Sometimes I'd wear it even if I'd forgotten to wash it. If it smelt bad, I would pretend to need the bathroom so I could spray it with deodorant and wash under my arms with hand soap. I was always doing things like this when I was younger:

sidling off to a toilet to reapply my make-up or pop a zit, or even change outfits if I'd caught my reflection in a window and thought that I looked fat. I never considered myself to be pretty, but when I turned eighteen I became acutely aware of my appearance, the way the backs of my legs might look to someone walking behind me, even the chubbiness of my fingers. My face was pocked with small patches of acne that never seemed to fade, and my hair was tough and straight and broken-ended in a way that reminded me of dried spaghetti, so I curled it every single day. When I stayed at my boyfriend's house I would even get up earlier than him so I could curl it before he woke up. I'd creep out of the bed, plug in the straighteners and quietly sit in front of the tiny mirror on his desk, anxiously winding handfuls of hair around the iron whilst checking that he wasn't suddenly awake and watching me. These moments were always so highly charged and frantic and not at all exciting. Even when it was done I would look at my desperate expression in the mirror and feel guilty or disgusting or both.

Despite this, when I moved to Edinburgh for university, I began to feel a strange, unfamiliar confidence in my situation. I carried myself differently, as though I mattered. Having an older boyfriend who played in a band filled me with the sense that I was different to my classmates. Wiser, cooler. I liked telling people that I was going to London for the weekend to watch his band play. Then I'd blow out smoke and change the subject as though I didn't really care anyway. The friends I made would ask if the distance between us bothered me, if I worried about what he might be doing in his free time. I told them that it didn't, but this was a lie. I clamoured for him during the weeks and sent him long text messages and stories and playlists I'd made for him online. If I knew he was out I would leave whatever I was doing and go home to sit in bed and wait for him to call. But in a way I enjoyed being apart from him too. It felt like I was being given extra time to make myself better. To get new clothes, to lose weight. If he told me that I looked thinner when we next saw each other, I would be happy all weekend. I would feel as though I'd achieved something and eat all the things I never let myself eat. It was always sad when we said goodbye, but on the train back I would fantasise about the days ahead of me, how much better I could be next time.

I thought about the conversation with my mother as I wondered about maybe buying porridge or cereals for breakfast again. This was another idea that I'd end up abandoning. This one has too many calories and this one has too much sugar. 'What's the point?' I'd said to her. 'Jacob broke up with her. She's allowed to sleep with someone if she wants to.'

'Of course she is,' my mother said, and I'd imagined her bristling up like a cat, snapping a dishcloth at the flies in the kitchen. 'It's not that she did it, that's not the problem. It's that she did it and she didn't tell him about it. Jacob hates dishonesty. I hate dishonesty.'

I'd wanted to say, 'Well, no one likes dishonesty.' But I didn't.

I walked down the bread aisle and saw a guy in uniform snapping REDUCED stickers onto packets of hotdog rolls and burger buns. He looked bored and the overhead lights gave his skin an oily sheen. We avoided making eye contact as I passed. I'd seen him working before at the tobacco stand. In fact I was in the supermarket so much that I recognised most of the people that worked there, though I always hoped they didn't recognise me. I only ever paid at the self-scanning checkouts as I didn't want the person serving to analyse the contents of my basket. I'd eaten a lot when I was a kid. I would spend all my pocket money on junk food and eat whole packets of biscuits alone in my bedroom. I was a small child, and I remember adults commenting on this, picking up my wrists and shaking them around. 'Just look,' they'd say, and I wouldn't get it because being slim isn't an achievement for children in the that way it is for adults. I got called 'pretty' a lot, and people were always giving me things like 20p coins or Freddo bars. I started to gain weight as I got older, though it wasn't something I particularly cared about. I remember sticking my belly out as I stood in front of the mirror in my sister's bedroom to make it look like my pregnant mother's, and I'd felt good then, like this was what becoming a woman was.

But when I started secondary school in a different town, I was overwhelmed by just how many other pupils there were, how easy it was for people not to like you. I got called names in the corridors by older boys who didn't know me, and everyone looked at each other in the changing rooms as we put on our PE kits. One boy in my class called me a *man whore*, and even though I didn't know what that was I thought that he was probably right. I started reading teen magazines a lot, where there were stories about girls who drank too much and push-up bras and what to wear on your first date. I wanted to look like the girls in the adverts, wanted short skirts and breasts that were high and round. I read an article about a girl who starved herself until her parents took her to a rehabilitation centre and I was envious of how emaciated she looked in the photographs.

Six months into our relationship, my boyfriend broke up with me and then slept with another girl, just like that. Like Jacob, his friend had told me about her, how he'd seen her messages on his phone, and I remember thinking, *I'll never eat again*. That same week I'd gotten drunk every night with whatever friends were up for it just so I felt too sick and tired to eat, and then suddenly he appeared outside my dorm building. He'd come all the way from Bristol to tell me that he was sorry, and it'd seemed like the most romantic thing to just turn up like that and ask to get back together. I wondered now if Jacob's girlfriend might do the same.

We were together for exactly three more weeks before he broke up with me again, and when he did I stayed in bed for two days. I told my mother about the whole thing, and she made my father drive her to Edinburgh to see me. They'd been divorced since I was three years old, but somehow they'd managed to stay reasonably friendly with each other. They took me out for lunch and told me all the things that should've made me feel better, that were meant to make me feel better, but instead made me feel even more pathetic. I'd picked the batter off the scampi on my plate as they said things like, 'You're so smart,' and, 'He just doesn't know what he's missing,' and I felt as though I might randomly projectile vomit. After that, I developed an irrational fear of throwing up, so I began to carry a sick bag around with me, just in case.

In the supermarket, I went to the frozen aisle to look at the desserts, which was something that I did a lot, and told myself that I could buy something and it would be a nice thing to do, to come home and say 'I got dessert!' and Ryan and I could eat dinner and watch TV and share a tub of ice cream, even a low calorie one.

On the phone, my mother had said, 'Do you remember how cut up you were, when that boy did the same thing to you all those years ago?'

At the time, a friend had told me that I would never forget what'd happened, but in actual fact I didn't think about it at all. I hadn't thought about it, really, until this evening. But sometimes in conversations I would listen to somebody talk about a cheating ex-partner and I would remember how quickly food can rush up from your stomach into your mouth. I could always recall the physical reactions, the dryness in your throat, the way your insides cramp when you haven't eaten for a day, but I never thought about emotional hurt or pain or crying. I was proud of myself for not letting it affect me, like I'd overcome something traumatic and was better for it.

I opened the freezer door and nearly reached out for a small carton of something dairy free that had NO SUGAR! NO FAT! written on the front in bright letters. I could cycle on the exercise bike I'd brought along with me when I moved in with Ryan a few months ago. We'd been together for two years, and he was very accepting of my insecurities. I felt as though, on some level, I'd begun to accept them too, even if in accepting that I would never be thin again also made me feel as though I'd failed. The glass was steaming up, so I shut the door and moved on and thought that it was probably best to not have anything at all because I'd only feel bad about it later. Ryan tells me that I worry too much, but I guess we're still learning to understand each other.

'Maybe you should send your brother a text or something,' my mother had said, 'just to let him know you're there for him,' and I started composing a text in my head as I walked towards the checkouts. *Hey Jacob, I heard about everything. So sorry, man. Sometimes these things happen and it sucks, but I really hope you're taking care of yourself.* I didn't even look at the shelves as I passed, instead I stared ahead at a blank woman scanning items at the conveyer belt on the other side. I focused on her with such intent that she appeared to shrink and stretch further away from where I was, no matter how close I got. Then it became a race and I started walking faster. *Hey Jake. Listen, she was a douche. Make sure you eat. You've got to eat.* Then I tried not to blink and I held my eyes open so they teared up and prickled but I kept going and I didn't blink at all and the shelves began to spin in the corners of my eyes but I looked straight ahead and I was holding my breath and soon the woman in her yellow T-shirt scanning dog treats and toilet rolls got bigger and bigger and I arrived at the other end lightheaded and new. *Hey Jacob, I'm so sorry to hear about what happened and I hope you're okay. This happened to me too when I was around your age and it feels really shitty, but it passes, I promise it does. You won't even remember it in the years to come.*

At the checkout there was a display of chocolate bars, and I thought about how good it would be to just be a person who buys one like it doesn't matter.

On the Far Side of the Thornbush

A ragged green field arrayed with
buttercups, daisies, and a small
settlement of recent yellow irises
springing out of a neat mound of
brown pony-dung, where a white
pony slow-swivels his big hieratic
head in my direction. Stopped like
that, he surveys me up and down,
then slowly turns and is a slow-
motion (for the moment) creature
until, with an electric twitch, he
sudden-gallops to become a beast
of fire until the barbed wire stops
him in his madcap pony-tracks
and he offers one quick inter-
rogative whinny at my departing
shape, his lonesome sphere-deep
black eyes finding my receding
shape and—with flicking ears and
quick inquisitive gaze—following.

Eamon Grennan

Atrophies

Cathy Thomas

The sun is melting on the horizon now, the clouds a trio of sorbet. A barbeque is flickering on the dunes below and Port Soif stinks like burnt beefburgers. The boys have got hotdogs in the boot of his car, cider and rum too, which they're saving for the bunker party later on. Paul checks his watch. It won't take long before they can get the evening going properly, knowing only too well how Tricky goes about his business.

Claire is already slithering on the bonnet with Tricky's hands on her, all over her, under her. The girl moans into Tricky's ear, her new full bottle of vodka clinking against the door keys to her gran's house in her handbag as she hitches herself higher up on the car. She gives Paul a wink.

Paul finishes his ciggy and walks to the other side of the car park. He has seen and heard this routine more times than he would care to remember. Every weekend, Claire gets off with Tricky so that he will buy her alcohol. Tricky doesn't have a car to get around, but Paul does; and Tricky is the one who gets them the gear for the parties, to which Jean-Christophe gets the invites. Exchanges like this make island life easy for everyone: there is always something to take and somewhere to go.

Paul no longer has an interest in using his ID to get girls, even though they stick to him like iron filings. Everyone starts young on the island, giving themselves longer to find genes that are different to their own. Paul wishes his dad had done that, for sure, his parents being Mahys and Le Maîtres, hundreds of years of local blood distilled into his neck and elbows. Think of the lobster pots you could've carried back in the day, his dad had said when as a child Paul cried about looking like such a Guern. Think of how rare it is to look like truly you belong to the land where you live.

Not that his dad says much these days, Paul thinks as he stubs out the fag-end on the dog litter bin and slouches back to the shelter of his car. Jean-Christophe opens the passenger door and clambers inside. Paul turns the car radio on.

I'm starving, Jean-Christophe says. Maybe we can go to the chippy before we go out.

Paul nods but he'd rather not spend the cash in his wallet if he doesn't need to. Paul hasn't sorted a steady job since leaving school and it's not like his dad tops him up.

I feel like getting fucked, Tricky says as he yanks open the car door. Paul can see Claire's silhouette slinking off towards her moped, pulling her hoodie over a flare of highlighted hair.

I'm starving, Jean-Christophe repeats. Can we go and get chips now?

Jean-Christophe has thick ropes of muscles across his body and he eats most hours of the day, drinking strawberry protein shakes in between snacks. If Jean-Christophe is the brawn and Tricky the brains—at least for sourcing what will make the night speed up—then that makes Paul the getaway driver.

Fine, but then we'll have to get some stash, Tricky says, raising his voice over the engine as Paul croons out of the cliff car park and back onto the coast road. Unless you've got anything at home?

Jean-Christophe and Paul say that they have nothing that'll get them high enough. Tricky pools their loose change as they pull up to the chip shop up at Cobo. You go in, Paul says, I'll drive round the block and wait.

He's relieved not to have to go inside, not wanting to have to make small talk with the girl from two years below at school who does the odd shift there. He can't remember if he's shagged her or not. When he was at school, Paul had won favour among the school's female population for taking their virginities, and although he would never have said that he really fancied many of them, it gave him a sense of purpose. But he had been so high most of the time that it was hard to remember who exactly he had done what with, or who he had flopped out on, and now he carries an awkwardness around in his pockets. When girls smiled at him down the Pollet or in the queue for the petrol pump, it used to make Paul feel liked; these days, he's finding it harder to be sure of who these people are and what they know of him. He has always felt sheltered by the shoulder-to-shoulder smallness of the island, but increasingly he is paranoid that it will catch him out.

I know exactly what you're doing, a teacher said to him the day he skipped his last A level exam in favour of the pub. I was just like you at your age. And you should be careful.

Careful not to turn into a shitty science teacher at my old school, you mean, sir? Paul had replied then, earning himself a litter-picking weekend.

Yet on nights like this, circling the chip shop in his Ford Fiesta, his anxiety tells him to take good care indeed. He is relieved when his friends emerge with warm white plastic bags dangling from their wrists like nappy sacks. He pulls over outside the co-op and they cram inside, their mouths already packed with vinegary chips and batter scraps. Paul drives to his favourite car park further south along the coast that's ensconced by bunkers and angular concrete Nazi fortifications staring out to sea. Sharp shadows range across the spume. He pulls up the car, its headlights cutting through the darkness just like the Hanois lighthouse in the distance, and puts on the handbrake. The windows steam up as the chips' wrapping paper wilts in their hands.

We could raid our parents' cupboards first, Tricky says. Prescriptions, painkillers. There might be something we can get for free. We can't turn up with just booze, we won't get into the party. What do you reckon your dad's got?

Codeine, antihistamine, betablockers and Ventolin: anything and everything could be put to use somehow. Paul doesn't fancy going home before they go out, but he can't think of a reason that isn't cut with a truth of sorts.

Paul's dad is asleep on the sofa when he gets in, an empty cider can crumpled beside the dog on the carpet. The dog tilts its nose up towards Paul's palm, snuffling at the smell of chips on his cuff. He picks up the empty can, along with two others from the coffee table that's piled high with outdated TV guides and crisping editions of *The Guernsey Press*, and bundles them into the kitchen bin. He opens the fridge, puts the two chilled cans from the third shelf into the bobbling pockets of his tracksuit bottoms. He takes a yoghurt and eats it with a tea-stained spoon that is propped on the side of the sink. There's no water in the dog bowl so he refills it before tramping up the stairs.

Josie, he calls up ahead. A stick of light shows beneath his younger sister's door. He knocks, readying one of the tins in his other hand as the price of entry. The tin gasps as he snatches open the ring-pull. There's no answer to his knock so he opens the door.

His sister isn't there but there is a tangle of vest tops on the floor and various eyeshadow compacts open on her desk. Bronzes, silvers, rough sea greys. Pencil eyeliners in mauve and black. He sits on her unmade bed, her bow-tied teddy plumped upon her pillows. Her room is awash with mess. He surveys the homework folders and textbooks slotted in the shelves along the wall, the bedstead hung with cheap beaded necklaces from their last family holiday to Nice. It was years ago, that trip, when his mum was still married to his dad and they still felt like a family. Josie had been nine then, pudgy-thighed with overgrown eyebrows and a home-cut fringe; now she's nearly fifteen. She's doing well at school, collecting more friends and grade As than he'd done at her age. But recently a razor has appeared on the side of the limescaled family bath and she has started to request nighttime lifts to Sausmarez Park. The bottles of spirits in the dining room cabinet, from which Paul himself sneaks finger-widths every weekend, are now emptying at a competitive pace. The one time he queried it, she'd snapped, Well maybe it's time you left home then. He wasn't sure whether she'd meant their dad's house or Guernsey, but he never asked.

He sups the sickly cider and looks at the photos tacked across her walls. Smiles and pigtails and blazing birthday cakes, beach volleyball and wetsuits and netball teams. He used to check her diary whenever she had an after-school club, at first to make sure that she wasn't in detention and later to make sure she hadn't got herself a boyfriend. He thinks about phoning her on the excuse of seeing if she needs a lift anywhere. At least then he'd know where she was. You're as bad as Dad, she'd said the last time he'd told her off for turning up twenty minutes late for her pick-up, and so he decides that tonight he'll leave her be. It's not like you can lose someone on an island this small. And he doesn't want Josie to despise him as much as they both despise their parents.

He finishes the end of the cider tin. Drinking and driving go together like whiskey and Coke on this island. Besides, Tricky's cousin's a policeman, so no one will rat on him as long as Tricky's in the car. Paul's never been caught anyway, whether at drink-driving or speeding on the Kev Run or phoning his sister while behind the wheel. None of his mates have ever been caught at anything. Paul opens the second cider with a hiss and lets the bubbles fall down his throat. It's stingingly sweet, but it is free. Another one less for his dad. He downs the rest of it and goes back out to his car.

The Kev Run is out in full force tonight: cars lined up, alloys shining, bass juddering from subwoofers. It's less of a drag race and more of a peacocking parade on the short stretch of the north-east coast road. An impressive car could get a guy a good Saturday job at a garage and get him into the right knickers. Plus, the racing offers a better adrenaline rush than surfing and punch-ups at the North Show, and the number of cars makes it an easy cover for drop-offs.

Paul and Tricky are sitting in the Fiesta, watching the Kev cars drive up and down. Their drug dealer hasn't showed yet, though they've been waiting for what feels like a waste of their evening. Paul scrutinises the young drivers outside: which ones are good, which are reckless, which might go on to take part in the official competitions with cash prizes.

Paul is a confident driver but hasn't fancied getting into racing since he saw someone scrape off half his cheek on the tarmac at the Val des Terres Hill Climb. He had been young enough then to cling onto his dad's hand, as if doing so would slow the car's speed as it whomped into a barrier amid the trees and wild garlic. That day, his mum had shouted and sniped at his dad for not bringing sun cream, slapping Josie's sunburnt arms as evidence. Josie cried and his mum went off to drink warm white wine from a plastic pint cup and flirt with someone else's dad. Paul didn't let go of his own father's hand until the paramedics had to break up the bystanders to get to the injured driver. They'd stood in the shade of the trees on the hill that looked out onto the town with its castle and bathing pools and shining sailboats, while the paramedics cut off the whining driver's clothes and rolled him onto a spinal board. Paul could hear his mum laughing somewhere. He remembered telling his dad how the biology teacher had said that our skin was an organ the same as our heart, our lungs, tongues, mouths, the small and large intestines both. His dad had taken a long time to reply, watching the paramedics tape the driver's matted head into a brace. Later, as Paul started dropping Josie off at school and putting fish fingers in the oven for her dinner, he would tell himself what his dad had said to him then: my skin is doing a difficult job, holding all my insides together like this.

The guy's clearly not coming, we should head, says Tricky through a clag of smoke. He flicks the burnished fag-end out of the window and onto the road. He turns to Paul and says, We'd better do a run up the Bouet if we want some stash.

Nothing's worth a run up the Bouet this time of night, Paul says. You'll have your arse bitten off by dogs. Or by Craig.

Craig owes me.

Craig never owes anyone anything, Paul knows. He has never met him in person but he has seen the apprehension in the eyes of younger dealers who work for him.

Craig owes me, Tricky repeats. He cut me short last time, thought I wouldn't notice. And we do need something. We can't go with nothing. You didn't find anything at home, did you?

No, Paul admits. But Jean-Christophe's still trying his parents'.

Nah, he'll have given up by now, Tricky says. He's meeting some girl before the party. He said he'll meet us there. It's up to us to get what we want. We're nearly at the estate anyway. Only round the corner. It'll take ten minutes. Come on. I'll do the talking.

But what if he's out?

Of course he'll be out, that's the point, Tricky says as he winds up the window. He'll be out on his rounds, all the kids will be having half-term parties this week, so he'll be up to his eyes in it.

Celeste opens the door. She opens the door enough for it to look friendly but not enough that the boys can see far beyond the brown sofa and the television that's not far off the sofa's size. Her legs are shiny with what looks like moisturiser and her hair is damp. The flat inside smells of shampoo and oven-baked garlic bread. A baby cries from somewhere.

Craig isn't in, she says.

I know he isn't, Tricky says.

Paul pushes his fingers into Tricky's forearm as a warning and says, We can come back.

I didn't know you had a little one, Tricky goes on, ignoring the dig of Paul's fingers, stepping towards the door frame and laying a rusk-like knuckle on the wood.

It's my neighbour's, Celeste says, instinctively looking behind her as if to check that the baby hasn't been kidnapped from the flat. I said I'd look after him tonight.

So you're the kind of person who can be trusted to know what to do, he says.

Why can't his mum look after him? Paul says.

We're in a bit of a hurry actually, Tricky says. Not much time to chat. He brings his other fist out of his pocket so that his arms form a barricade on the door. Can we come in now?

Paul has never hit a woman, and is sure as he can be that Tricky hasn't and wouldn't. He tries to picture Craig with Celeste, what their relationship would look like. Paul knows that Celeste is younger than she looks because she was only three years above him at school. Celeste had lived in Forest then, and their dads had been friendly to each other at cross-country pick-ups, and sometimes in the school holidays she'd babysit him and his sister. Josie had looked up to her, as any girl would look up to someone older who knew how to smoke and do eyeliner. He wonders what Josie would think now of Celeste's brittle hair and bitten nails, the rawness of her eyes and marks up her arms. He tries hard not to stare.

What is it? Celeste looks from Paul to Tricky.

Craig wants us to do a drop-off for him, Tricky carries on. He's too busy himself and he needs more supply.

Is that true? she asks Paul.

Paul sways slightly from the evening's cider and squints as the strip lighting ices his eyeballs. Sure, he says, as if one word can't make a lie.

We don't want to keep Craig waiting. We don't want to get into shit with him, Tricky says as he shoulders her out of the doorway and pushes on inside into the flat.

You might as well come in too then, Celeste says finally to Paul, following Tricky into the lounge and scooping up the baby off the sofa cushions before he can get a look at it. She jiggles the bundle of blankets up and down in her arms as she watches the boys for their next move. She says very quietly over the baby's hairless scalp, I hope you know what you're doing.

Where is it? Tricky says.

You mean he asked you to do a job for him but didn't tell you? Celeste replies.

Paul expects Celeste to protest, or shout, or throw something, but she sits down and stares at Paul. She doesn't even get her phone out. Maybe this has happened to her before and she knows it's easier not to get involved. With Craig as a boyfriend, Paul imagines that she must try not to get involved all the time.

Tricky begins to open drawers, lift up knickknacks, shove discarded clothing across the floor with his shoes. He shakes open gossip magazines and scatters cigarettes from a carton onto the tea-marbled coffee table. Where's the bedroom? he says, not waiting for an answer.

Why would you be dealing for Craig? Celeste asks. You're not really, are you?

Paul shrugs.

I'm not thick, she says, keeping her hands busy with the baby squirming on her knee. I just hope you're not either.

Is his mum going to be alright, Paul says with a nod at the baby. Paul's struggling not to sink back into the sofa as the warmth punches out from the electric heater balanced in front of it. They should've gone straight to the bunker party without the drugs: they shouldn't have come here. It's difficult not to keep an eye on the door in case Craig makes an entrance and mashes them into the carpet.

Is his mum going to be alright? repeats Celeste, extracting her earrings from the baby's hand. Look around you. Open your eyes too wide and you'll fall off your perch.

Paul doesn't want to look at anything here anymore. He considers going to see how Tricky is getting on but he would rather not rifle through underwear drawers and make-up bags. There is the china clink of the cistern lid being replaced. Paul needs a glass of water but he doesn't want to ask Celeste for it. The guilt suppurates beneath the booze and he can feel the night tipping over.

What does your dad think about your new line of work?

Paul looks at her and then catches the shock of his expression in the reflection of the black TV screen. He looks really small sitting down.

How's your dad doing anyway? she says.

He's alright, Paul says.

I read in the *Press* about him, poor fuck, she says. Even on an island this small you can't get far without a car. How long's he going to be off the roads for?

He's alright, Paul repeats.

Still living at home with him, yeah? And your sister?

Her too, he says.

I always liked your sister. And your mum? How's she?

I wouldn't know.

It's not that far to find out, surely.

Not when she's got a new family, Paul says.

You're a nice boy, I always thought, Celeste says. Did your homework when I asked you, always finished what was on your plate. But I thought you would've grown up more by now. What are you doing for work, really?

What's your point? he says. Paul considers going to the kitchen to fetch himself a drink but would rather have Celeste report back at the end of the night that he wasn't the one to actually nick anything. He used to think that if he drove the car and the others were the ones who did the deals or the fights, that he would still technically be a good guy.

Do you know what it's like to get beaten up, Paul, like properly? Celeste says.

Why are you with him then? Paul snaps, listening out for how Tricky is getting on. He's taking his time: a luxury in a place like this.

I'm no more a victim than you are, Celeste says. You're asking the wrong questions.

The baby burps and she bobs it on her lap, rubbing its tiny curled back. The legs of the babygro are too long for him, so that his feet poke out where his knees should be. Bubbles of spit shine on his lips and chin.

Tricky emerges with a square of tinfoil shining through his white T-shirt pocket. He's grinning, sweating from pride and from substances tried and tested.

He'll run you off the roads, Celeste says. Good luck on the Kev when your eyes are bleeding out your nose.

He can't be that bad, Paul says.

That's sweet, she says.

Tricky is already laughing his way down the stairs and away from the estate, clanging his house keys along the metal railings. Paul turns to follow.

Paul, Celeste shouts after him as he tries hard not to turn around and look. I saw your mum down the co-op last week with her new kids and she was looking really fucking happy.

Anxiety starts to jigger Paul's vision so that once they're halfway across the island towards the west coast, he has to pull the car over. The yellow lines reflect the headlights back into the night. The driveway belongs to La Houguette Primary School, its schoolhouse and SLOW CHILDREN traffic signs starkly silhouetted. The island's police tend to check the cliff car parks most for dogging and dealers, so school properties could always be relied upon to be lead-lined quiet at this time of night.

Give that, Paul says to Tricky, who is thumbing a fat joint between his fingers.

You've finally lost it, Tricky laughs. I've never seen anyone look so scared. If you're scared of Celeste, mate, just wait till Craig gets hold of you.

Do you think she'll tell him? Paul says. He won't actually come after us?

Why, what are you going to do? Leave? Drive to the mainland? Tricky is howling with laughter now.

Paul breathes in deeply and hands the joint back to Tricky. If he rides out the nausea he'll feel calm enough to drive again soon. Going to the party will take his mind off it, he knows, but they've got to get there first and he can feel the night closing off the unlit lanes like trapdoors.

Tricky and Paul grew up together. They know the local lanes better than the cracks on their bedroom ceilings and they know what to say to wind the other up. But what Paul is starting to forget is what it had been like before. Before there was porn and vodka and seven per cent cider and roll-ups and joints and aerosols and wraps and pills and late nights and insomnia and red eyes and shaving cuts and car crashes and overdrafts. Before, there had been surfing and cliff-jumping and Sunday roasts and birthday barbeques and pocket money; before, he could start a half-term holiday and decide for himself what he wanted to do. Somehow the last few years have rolled into one bad night out.

What are we actually going to do? Paul says. Tricky is giggling. Tricky giggles until Paul's breathing slows and he feels calm enough to start the ignition and let the condensation slide off the windscreen. Maybe it's the joint but he has the feeling that he won't find anything hilarious ever again.

There's a bunker by the Table des Pions just over the Pleinmont headland, past the old greenhouses stretched out across the fields, sagging and splintering in the weeds. Up the sharp path through the spindly woods where the alcoholic from the now-closed Mercedes garage hanged himself last year, but just before you get to the stone fairy circle and the rocks carved by a slave worker during the war. The sea looks medieval from up here, mystic. It's good spot for a party, and this is where a lot of the best parties happen.

It's early now, or late to Paul, the moonlight smudging on the slapping sea. DROP IT LIKE IT'S HOT, the music thrusts from within. There is a haze hanging over the bunker's entrance from the hash, cut through by strobes of light from the Hanois lighthouse. A wind is getting up over the water, dragging out the musk from the bunker. The smell is Turkish Delight sweet.

It's a fiver to get inside and as soon as you do, there's a makeshift table of mixed beers and spirits, which everyone is welcome to dip into so long as they make a contribution too. Paul adds their rum and cider to the offering. There are people on the floor, slid across cushions and sacking and plastic bags split open at the sides. Danny Torode is caning lines from a patio table and the sixth form kid from Alderney is picking out a melody on a guitar. Someone is DJing in one of the dark passageways that spike off from the central concrete chamber. A string of fairy lights is strung up along another, flickering every so often when someone stumbles on the freestanding generator. Claire will be around somewhere with her vodka, so Tricky disappears off into one of the dank channels, tipping the peak of his baseball cap down so that it doesn't scrape the lichen lining the low ceiling.

They don't do parties like this in Winchester, Helen Dorey is saying to whoever will listen. She's back from her art foundation course for reading week, during which she claims she hasn't read a thing but has instead accumulated multiple lovers and some fucking funny stories, yeah. There are those here who are still at school, those who have been away to university on the mainland and since returned, those who never left. He's thankful that he can't see anyone from his old year at school as he's not in the mood to discuss what he's doing now and why he's still here. But nobody moves to involve him in conversation at all and somehow that feels worse, like it's because they already know the answers.

Paul considers the booze on the table, aware that Tricky has walked off with their wrap tucked in his pocket. He punches open a tin of cider and picks his way across the muddled floor towards an empty spot, where he perches himself on an upturned keg. He feels lighter with fresh booze in his blood. Holding the tin gives him something to do with his hands. He drinks a bit more, feels the booze sloping his shoulders, settles on his seat. In the shadows, he feels less self-conscious. This is what Paul likes best at gatherings, get-togethers, piss-ups and parties: watching the crowd. And there is always someone in the crowd at these dos who has undone themselves, through drinking too much or choking or boasting about how much coke they could take when they'd never had a sniff of a line before. The best entertainment at any party is the mistakes of other people.

There is a girl in the corner who's lazing around by herself, her hair draped over her face. Paul has been watching her, trying to work out if she's drunk or asleep, whether she's too far gone, whether she's just enjoying whatever she's taken. He can't work out if it's someone he got with one, two years ago: she seems familiar enough. She still doesn't move for a good few minutes so he goes over to her just to check. She doesn't look up when he asks if she's okay and he turns her onto her side.

It's Josie. His sister smells like the caustic apple flavouring of the spirit dribbling from the green bottle in her hands. Her legs are open slightly and he catches the golden sheen of her metallic bikini bottoms as he kneels down to pick her up. Her eyes are sticky and struggling in the half-light. He is glad he found her before anyone else.

Josie, he says, pulling her top down over her bare stomach. Come on, he's saying, Come with me. He slots his forearms under her armpits and hauls her out of the chamber, her limp feet curling through empty cans on the floor. He thinks of Celeste carrying her neighbour's baby, thinks how Celeste would carry Josie up the stairs to bed after she fell asleep watching television. None of the other partygoers turn to look at him as he hefts his sister out into the smeared morning; it's not the first time that someone came to a bunker party before they were ready, and nobody's really ready for their first time. Her thick breathing wets the shoulder of his top as he carries his sister over the dewy gorse towards the car. He isn't angry with her, he thinks, she's just doing what he's always done.

The sun is rising on the back of the wind. The waves crunch over the pebbles like crisp packets. Some of Paul's mates take pleasure in saying that the island is boring, it's a heap of shit, it's backwards, it's full of inbreds and pissheads and can you imagine being one of those people who never leave? But Paul looks across the sea and back to the headland, to the bunker with its seething music behind him, and he sees that it is beautiful. He loves this island, not in spite of the boredom and his angry cousins and drunk dad and the curly fries served in plastic baskets at the Bowl and the pride of the Kev Run and all the puny parties, but because of all these things. It is his home and the early mornings like this one on the cliffs are filled with colours you wouldn't see anywhere else. He knows that leaving is never an option for him, and that he's not just staying for his sister either.

He opens the back door of his Fiesta and marshmallows his sister's body onto the back seat. Her head lolls over the upholstery so he takes off his sweatshirt and rolls it up into a pillow for her. He'll drive Josie home, tuck her into bed. Then he'll get into his own bed and sleep off his hangover for as long as he needs to.

Wait, Tricky calls out from the bunker, emerging from the darkness into the morning warmth. Hang on.

I'm going home, Paul says and pulls the car door shut.

Just a favour for a couple of hours and then you can fuck off with your girl, Tricky says, rapping on the window so that Paul has to wind it down. Tricky frowns at the shock of Josie sprawled on the back seat.

We're going home, Paul says.

He places his hands either side of the wheel. Like you're drying the dishes, his driving instructor had always said. The shake in his hands, Paul could smash the crockery all over his dad's kitchen floor in this state. He can feel a vein pipping in the inner crease of his left elbow. His fingers leaving sweat prints on the faux leather. He puts the keys in the ignition and tells Tricky out the window, I'm done.

Craig's found out we've nicked his stash, Tricky says.

So what? Paul says. He was always going to.

We've got to get to him before he gets to us.

I'm not getting in a fight with Craig.

Of course not, you couldn't fight a fish, Tricky says. But you can drive me there and I'll have a go.

No way I'm driving up to the Bridge like this.

It's only round the coast, Tricky says. You could drive there with your bollocks.

Paul winds up the window but Tricky wedges his hand in the way.

Do you want to see my teeth knocked out on a scaffolding pole, Tricky says.

No but—

Are you sure?

But my sister, Paul says.

So what, he says, getting into the passenger seat. We can drop her off first.

Pulling into the cul-de-sac where he lives, Paul persuades Tricky to help carry her out of the car and up the stairs. Tricky cradles her knees and Paul hooks his fists under her armpits, and they slouch her onto her single bed. Paul tells Tricky to piss off back outside while he sorts her out. Paul takes his sister's trainers off, balls up her socks, arranges the duvet covers over her. Her make-up is butchered across her skin but she is peacefully asleep. He turns her head on one side so that her cheek is on the pillow and moves the bin near. He sits on the edge of her bed, one hand resting over her blanketed feet, and takes a breath. Then he slips down to the kitchen to fetch a glass of water, fills the glass right to the top, and takes it up to Josie's bedside. He places it just out of reach so that she won't knock it over.

A car door slams outside and Paul goes to the window to check who it is. No Craig yet. He pictures Tricky on the backseat waiting for him, bouncing his forehead on the headrest and rummaging amongst the empty chip wrappers on the floor for a chance quid. Perhaps Tricky was clever for failing his driving theory test all along.

Paul tweaks the curtains shut so that Josie won't get woken up by the light earlier than she needs to. He is aware that he hasn't slept for a long time, not properly. His blood feels carbonated, caffeinated. He closes her bedroom door gently and pads downstairs, closing the front door behind him with his key turned in the lock so that it barely makes a sound. Then he walks towards his car, where Tricky is now waiting in the passenger seat, rolling his next joint for him.

Practice, Process, Product

Mia Gallagher

This is the text of a lecture commissioned by The Stinging Fly and delivered at Bray Literary Festival on 28 September 2019.

Definitions

Let me start by offering you my definitions of what the terms product, process and practice mean in relation to writing. These aren't universal truths: they are my personal interpretations, built up through experience.

Product to me is, firstly, the outcome of writing: a Thing that is made using words. It can be a book, play, poem, collection, performance, essay, article—or any other piece of writing you can think of. This lecture, for example, is a writing product. But there's a second writing product: the self-as-writer. In my case, this is: 'novelist Mia Gallagher' or 'novelist and short-story writer Mia Gallagher'.

Process, to me, is also twofold. Firstly, it's the way in which a piece of writing gets made. This includes the time spent making the work, the technical methods used, and any breakthroughs, blocks, revisions or challenges along the way. This process ends when I sign off on my final proofs—there's nothing more to write. The secondary writing process is the formation of self-as-writer-of-a-particular-product. For example: 'Mia Gallagher, debut author of *HellFire…*' or 'Mia Gallagher, whose latest book is the short-story collection *Shift…* ' The secondary process starts the moment the product is publicly announced—in a biog (biography), reading, interview, or Q&A—and it lasts until the next product is announced.

Practice, to me, is the entire life of the writer as dedicated to making Things from words. It encompasses many different products and the processes that go into their making. It also includes the cumulative making of self-as-writer through the sequential formation of self-as-writer-of-particular-products.

A writer's practice can't continue after they die, though their works might endure, their processes might be borrowed and adapted by other writers, and they as writer-product may survive as legacy, continuing to be interpreted, internalised and working as an influence on other writers. For example: I love 'Angela Carter'.

Product

Special

We live in a period of late capitalism: fast, global, technological, peppered by rapid-fire crises of accumulation, aka boom and bust. At its simplest, capitalism is driven by two motors. These are profit—selling Things, including books, for more than they cost to make. And growth—the never-ending increase of profit. Capitalism is, essentially, a giant pyramid scheme. The gold tends to flow upwards, the shit tends to get shoved downwards. Both can be diverted in the opposite direction, but only if governments have the will to regulate accordingly.

When capitalism, powered by the Industrial Revolution, swapped its tricycle with stabilisers for a 5-speed racer in the 19th century, Romanticism emerged as an ideology. It's from Romanticism that we get the idea that artists, including writers, are somehow outside the capitalist pyramid. Because we're 'creative', we're exempt. We're the special ones, the wise ones, the talented ones, commenting on and understanding how everything works, transforming the world through our amazing words, but somehow never prey to its vagaries.

Although we're long past Romanticism's heyday now, this idea has lingered. Partly because it's so seductive—who doesn't want to stand out? But it comes with a mess of baggage that still creates problems for artists in their working lives. I've been at several public events where writers have been hailed as 'geniuses' in the sort of doting, baffled tones reserved for a favourite child, the one whose 'condition' it's not polite to bring up in company. Then times get rough and the same people, talking about the same writer, who is now seeking funding, get snippy. Bloody spongers, they say, why doesn't she get up in the morning and find a proper job? Why should he get grants when doctors (or farmers or teachers or…) don't? Besides—the killer line—sure you're not doing it for the money, are you?

I imagine you're all familiar with the bullshit misconceptions that accompany the idea of artistic 'specialness'. For example: Writers are terrible with money. Or: Writers don't care about money. As one woman in an art class once said to my husband, who's a visual artist: Sure what do you need money for? Then there's the: Oh, you artistic types are all away with the fairies. Bad at organising. Off the wall. Like kids. Working with you writers, an arts administrator told me after an international literary exchange, was like herding cats. For all this, read 'irresponsible'.

Every ideology, every codified system of looking at the world, serves an end. There's a question here I'm not sure I can answer. Who benefits from these misconceptions? Most writers I know are highly organised, numerate, money-conscious and thrifty. They bring in the vast majority of their projects on time and under budget, in a way the private and public sectors could learn from. Who or what is threatened by the possibility that artists may, in fact, be responsible?

No writer is more special than any other human. I, like you, am just like all other citizens, trying to survive and do what what's most meaningful for me, inside the pyramidal socio-economic system we call capitalism. Every writer—and every distributor of their work, even the smallest, most 'artistically minded' publisher—is operating within this system's confines and complying with its unwritten rules.

Now don't get me wrong: there are great things about capitalism. It's given me my washing machine and Sky Box Sets. I'd hate to ditch it completely. But its twin pillars are killing us. Profit first means somebody, somewhere, is being exploited. Infinite economic growth on a finite planet means something, somewhere has got to give.

If we focus in on the writing life and map the rules of the pyramid there, particular types of pressures emerge.

Write more words. Write them faster. Make them into a Thing that can be sold. Get that Thing published. Write more Things that appeal to more people. Write them so the company distributing them can make more money. Make more money from the current Thing than the last Thing. Get more reviews. Get more reviews with more positive adjectives in them. Get more ratings on Amazon. Win an award. Sign a TV or film deal. Sign both. Sign more. Sign them faster. Win the Goldsmiths. Win the Booker. Win the Impac. Win an Emmy. Win the Nobel. Grow your brand. Become bestselling-writer-self. Become multi-award-winning-writer-self. Become global-superstar-writer-self. Then, and only then, will you be really special.

Value

Success and value, as Marx discussed, are shifting qualities. Like weight, they vary according to the field of gravity they're being measured in. A penny is lighter on the moon. The gravity field you and I operate in is capitalism, where value is measured through financial profit and economic growth. Through this lens, 'successful' writing is primarily about the production and sales of sellable Things—the writing product and the writer-as-product.

The problem with product-focused success in a capitalist economy is that, if I buy into it, I will outsource my ability to value my own work. Most products succeed or fail outside the self. Take a rivet which holds an aeroplane wing together. Either it works or it doesn't; and any engineer worth their salt can objectively calculate the extent to which it does or doesn't do its job. The financial value of the rivet is also externally measurable, through stock and share prices, at any moment. But how writing 'works'—how it lands with readers—is subjective. Each reader experiences their own internal response to it. As a writer, I can only access this by what, if anything, they publicly say about the work and what, if anything, they pay me for it. If I use these measures, and these measures alone, to value my writing, I will become dependent on others to 'buy' me or 'sign' me, to 'praise' me or 'award' me—to 'get' me—in order to feel that what I am doing is worthwhile.

Applying the law of averages, 50 per cent of people are likely to get what I write and 50 per cent aren't. Not the toughest odds in the world, but not a clear run either. If I completely outsource my value as a writer by relying on others to always 'get' me, I set myself up for a life of disappointment, resentment, frustration, jealousy, occasional hatred, insecurity, despondency, despair and, finally, inaction. Anytime that I've got overly product-focused and put pressure on myself to write faster, more, or bigger, to get published quicker or to generate more money from my writing, I've ended up stopping.

Now I need to name the elephant in the room. While I, like you, am making work within capitalism, I've been awarded a status that helps me navigate some of these pressures. Last year I was elected to Aosdána, so I'm now entitled to seek five-year tranches of funding as long as my other income falls below a certain threshold. This is a privilege. It's also a clear external indicator of value. So in real terms, it's far easier for me to stand here and talk this way than it would be for a writer who isn't grant-funded to the same extent.

However, even with that caveat, I'm still, like most of you, susceptible to the pyramid's pressures. I still need to write, I still want to make writing products, and I'm still invested in my self-as-writer product. Pain comes up for me if a piece is rejected, or if I hear about colleagues signing big money deals or winning big awards. I get jealous, I get sad, I get down. Then the self-flagellation starts. I must be doing something wrong. I'm not as good as I think I am. And on and on. I'm sure most of you have had similar experiences.

During the last decade, I had a particularly rough five years where my second novel was lingering on publishers' desks. Nobody was 'getting' it. Nobody wanted to buy it. One day, in a single phone call with my agent, I got six rejections. Those five years taught me a lot—mainly how addicted I was to external validation. To survive as a writer, I had to learn to go inwards instead. That took time, but what helped most was learning to replacing the idea of *More* with *Better*. Instead of *More* words, write *Better* words. Write *Better* books. This, of course, is tricky too. What is 'Better'? What *The Irish Times* says? What Twitter says? Amazon? Whatever wins the Booker? I'll say it again, because it's important: if I give the power to anybody else to define what 'good' or 'Better' writing are, I'll end up in trouble—insecure, dependent again on others 'getting' me.

For me, 'Better' changes by the day, but essentially it's the feeling that I'm doing something new or unexpected with the writing. I've made a discovery and it's surprised me. 'Better' isn't a mental judgement on 'good writing'; it's a feeling, an emotional-attitudinal state. *Yeah. Okay. Oh! This works.* It's NOT: 'Oh God, *The Guardian* will love this.' The closest I've come to defining 'Better' is the idea of being able to stand over the work. This means understanding what my unconscious intentions are, what I want the piece to do; then, through interrogating those intentions, being happy that they come from the right place; and being—more or less—happy that, at the end of the process, the work has achieved what it set out to do.

Writing Better isn't something I do in isolation. I have a terrific agent who understands where I'm coming from, and I've worked with excellent editors, like Dan Bolger, Declan Meade and Patricia Deevy, who get me. These people are great sounding boards; they help me sense if something is 'Better' or 'could be Better' and they often see things I can't. But in the end, *I* have to stand over the work, and it's that inner feeling—yes, no, uh oh—which is the truest measure of value to me. It's that sensation—not praise or an index on the stock exchange—that tells me if, and how, the Thing is 'working'. It's that which gives me the deepest sense of my authority as a writer and helps me duck out, even briefly, from product fixation.

I've had to learn to connect with this instinct, I've had to learn to trust it. I've done lots of what's loosely called 'work on myself': developing my emotional intelligence through pain, trauma, and recovery, usually under the guidance of experienced somatic practitioners. What's also helped is reading and critiquing other writers. I always try to do this as a reader first, not an expert. How does this work make me feel? What does it make me want? What does it give? Listening to instinct while reading other people exercises the muscle. In turn, I can apply it Better to my own work. And then I can keep going deeper, finding the new, redefining 'Better'.

Marx talked about exchange-value—what people agree something is worth—versus use-value, what the Thing is functionally used for. A bank note has no use value; it has massive exchange value. That aeroplane rivet has a low exchange value, but high use-value. Works of writing—yours, mine, anyone's—are repositories of meaning. Some people will get the meaning, some won't. But meaning is their function, their use-value as Things in the world. If I, or you, can be responsible for this function, if we can quality test it as much as possible, then I, or you, might be able to put our meaning-holders out into the world without obsessing all the time about their exchange-value, the value the world attributes to them.

Easier said than done, but try it.

Branding

Mia Gallagher is a novelist and short-story writer based in Dublin, blah blah blah...

A biog looks like a small thing, but in fact, it's a point of power.

Like the primary writing product, the writer-product comes in many guises: some are singular ('poet'), some dual or hybrid ('storyteller and librettist' or 'essayist-playwright'). Every writer whose work is publicly available is stamped as a product through the organs of publicity—reviews, promotional material, interviews, features and the biography the writer themselves sends out with their work.

How a product is stamped is called, in marketing, branding. A brand is a contract. *Trust me*, it says, *I will do what I say I will.* Daz washes our whites whiter. 8 out of 10 cats prefer Whiskas. Johnson will get Brexit done. But because most writers write their own biogs—self-branding-self—the biog is not like other brands. It is another writing product by that writer, and a particular type: a product that indicates the attitude of self to the pyramid scheme the self-as-writer-product is being sold through.

One of my favourite biogs is the one Lia Mills uses. It starts: *Lia Mills writes novels, essays and stories…* What I love about it is how it doesn't what-ify Lia. Lia is Lia. The biog refuses to categorise her as a novelist, essayist or short-story writer, or even a hybrid. She is not a Thing. Writing is what she does. It is active; she is the actor. It takes a certain amount of psychological confidence to write a biog like that. As I parse it I'm starting to think it's quite a revolutionary little comment. Fuck you and your products, Lia's biog seems to say. I'm me. Brand me all you want but I refuse to reduce myself to a single consumable Thing. In a gender-unequal world where, to paraphrase the late John Berger, men still act while women still appear, Lia's statement of action seems even more radical.

People started calling me 'a novelist' in 2006, after my first book *HellFire* was published, but I felt embarrassed using that word about myself. It seemed fraudulent. I'd had two stabs at writing novels before, but one I'd never finished and the second had never been published. By 2006, I was well into the process of struggling with a new novel, but I didn't know if I'd ever complete it. Surely an 'ist' is someone who does something regularly? How could I be a novel-ist until I'd written more than one novel and been publicly acknowledged as having done so—i.e. had my second book 'out'?

Fretting and insecure, I plumped instead for *Mia Gallagher is the author of…*, and because I was desperate to prove that I was, in fact, a writer-product and therefore special, I filled out the rest of my biog with lists of where my stories had been published and examples of my theatre work.

Seven years later, in 2013, the novel I'd been struggling with when *HellFire* came out had garnered twenty-plus rejections. Extracts were being published, but there was no guarantee the whole book would find a home. However, I had just spent a year reworking it, going deeper into the story, making it Better. It was during that process that I remember thinking, ah, so this is what a 'novelist' is. It's a person who makes novels. It was then, three years before the book—*Beautiful Pictures of the Lost Homeland*—was published, that I started using the word to describe my self-as-writer.

Though I love Lia's biog, the 'journey'—to use that awful phrase—to get me to the point where I could call myself a 'novelist' still feels too fresh and hard-won to relinquish. I'm not yet secure enough to drop that branding. Maybe when I've finished my third novel. The one I'm stuck on right now. Maybe then I'll be able to say, with conviction, *Mia Gallagher writes novels and other Things*.

What do you call yourself? How do you brand yourself? What product are—and aren't—you?

Processs

Efficiency

This August, during a residential programme in Dingle, I listened to Ann Hood and Andre Dubus III, two American authors, talk about writing friendships. They spoke of sitting down with other writers to talk about craft, and I was struck by how delighted they were when they mentioned this. All writers I know love talking about process. It's safer than product because it's an internal experience and other people can't judge it. And it's always interesting, because it's where the learning happens. Recently Arlen House brought out *The Danger and the Glory*, a collection of writings by Irish writers on process, and it's well worth a look.

In a product-focused system like capitalism, process is about making profitable Things. To maximise profit, process needs to become efficient. Efficiency means conserving time, 'rationalising' labour by separating out tasks and the workforce doing those tasks, and, in many cases, automating. The aim is More, but also faster, smoother, more systematic. Everywhere I look I see capitalism's holy grail of efficiency seeping into writing websites, courses and supports. How to Write a Novel. NaNoWriMo. Ten Tips for Creating Characters.

In any line of work, it's important to be able to access the experience of others further along the road. I've benefited from standing on giants' shoulders, and I've also benefited—both economically and in terms of skills—from running How To and other courses. But there's something about the How To ethos that troubles me. It makes me wonder what the point of writing is. To make more books, and make them faster? Does the world need more books, faster-made?

Endless growth?

Nothing in nature grows infinitely.

The problem with efficiency is that it's a rational construct: bright, formulaic, clear. Writing is logical, but logical is not the same as rational. The logic followed by imaginative writing—and I include memoir and essay writing here—is that of the unconscious. The unconscious isn't bright. It's like ghosts; it needs the shadows to thrive. Become too formulaic, too clear, and the unconscious will baulk.

Like all writers, I love making technical discoveries: for example, finding out how to let the reader know what a character is feeling without necessarily telling them. In the best case scenario, a discovery like this will infuse the work with an extra layer of meaning that makes it Better. But if I keep applying the discovery like acne cream, like it's the 'right' way, or the only way, to reveal character interiority, then I'm fucked. The text starts getting peppered with crafty devices, that, if I'm not careful, become my 'thing'. Then it becomes a 'Mia Gallagher thing' and then it's boring and it all goes to shit. As David Foster Wallace said: the problem with a discovery is it becomes a habit; the problem with habit is it becomes a tic.

Who wants tics in their writing? And I ask this sincerely, because some tics, when expertly handled, can coalesce into genre, and genre is a beautiful, fun, comforting Thing. More black-coffee swiggin' haymaker-punchin' Jack Reacher? Yes, please.

In Andrew Simonet's excellent text, *Making Your Life as an Artist*, he talks about how artists are often judged as if they're sportspeople. Who wins, who's the fastest, who's the strongest, who can jump the highest. In sports there's only room for one winner. Simonet argues that artists, in fact, are more like scientists. We ask questions, we experiment with finding answers, we fail, we try again. Winning doesn't come into it, or if it does, it's only momentarily. While my second novel was languishing on editors' desks, Simonet's insights helped me navigate my own attitude towards failure, helped me realise that I should be failing; as should you. We should all be failing, and failing more.

Via Negativa is the name given to a learning process built around failure. I learn by making mistakes, not by getting it right. The child doesn't stand up one day from a supine position and instantly start running. They roll, they tumble, they sit, they fall, they tumble, they sit, they twist, they fall, they rise, they step, they fall, they tumble, they roll.

When I'm writing Things, especially novels, I get stuck for at least as much time as I am in flow. This, I try to tell myself, is good. Go into it, I tell myself. Find the pain in the stuckness, dig into it, under it. Face it, whatever way it comes up. Oh, I feel terrible, Oh, I'm such a shit writer, Oh, this book will never get finished.

In the face of that feeling, I try to ask myself *What*. What is so shit about this book, story, or essay? What isn't working? Usually, after a while, answers come. The character, I don't believe them. The world is flimsy. It feels pointless writing this stuff when the rainforest is burning. These are all valid responses. I try to listen to them. Then I try to ask the next *What*. What don't I believe in? If I'm lucky, a *What if* comes. What if this novel is about pointlessness? This sounds easy, but it takes time.

Write like you're a scientist.

Obvious

In the 1990s I worked on a digital project called *Courage to Create*, designed for a now defunct platform, CD-i. The producer, Áinne Burke, had come from the visual arts world and worked in TV before moving onto what was then called 'new media'. Áinne was big into process and one of the keystones of her project was that the dynamics of generating and exploring an idea are different to those involved in learning technical skills, different in turn to how we internalise story content and form, and different again to the ways in which we realise a finished work. What most struck me was the idea that there's no right way to produce a work, but that there are areas of work-making, each with its own challenges. A 'problem' in one can lead to the whole project stalling. So if, for example, I want to write a family epic and I understand how to craft sentences but haven't spent enough time researching the world that family is born into, then sooner or later, in spite of my technical skills, the epic will become an epic fail.

Áinne's main aim was to encourage audio-visual makers to stay with the initial stages of the work as much as possible. Pay attention to their imagination, nourish their dreams, mine their memories, and listen to those weird blurts that pop up from their unconscious. Try to cohere or solidify these too quickly, she argued, and the ideas will shrivel up and die. I see it a bit like turning the lights on at a disco during the slow set.

Over ten years later, in 2007, I attended a seminar in Pearse Street Library where I heard another Áine talk about process. This time it was Áine McCarthy—aka author, journalist and publisher Orna Ross, who was giving a seminar on seven stages of novel-writing, from gestation to final refinement. At the time I was feeling frustrated and stuck with my second novel. Listening to Orna, I realised the problem wasn't with the book, but with the fact that I was trying to refine something that hadn't even found its initial shape yet. I started exploring again, going back to the early stages, listening to my unconscious—memories, dreams, imagination, blurts—getting lost. Eventually, three years later, the book reached first draft.

Recently I had a chat with a writer who was stuck. She wanted my opinion on a technical issue she thought was the heart of her problem. Her project involves crafting non-fiction stories out of interview material and she was trying to figure out what point of view to choose for her draft. Should she go for different points of view for each interview, or a single overarching one? It was wrecking her head. After a few minutes it became clear that the issue wasn't point of view at all, but that, like me, she thought she was at a different stage of the process to where she actually was. She hadn't yet transcribed all the interviews. I suggested she do that first, as a task to keep the front part of her mind busy. A quasi-meditation. In the meantime, keep mulling over point of view, jot down any ideas that came to her. Go to the haberdasher's to buy fabric before you start making the dress.

Do the basic thing first. Attend to your unconscious, jot down what it says. Always try the bloody obvious. Always follow a *What if*.

Gardening

Neil Gaiman talks about two 'types' of writers: gardeners and architects. Gardeners plant seeds but don't know which ones will take. Architects create blueprints, exact impressions of the final Thing. I'm wary of any formulas, particularly my own, but if I had to choose, I'd say I'm a gardener first, then an architect.

Right now, I'm stuck on—in—a new book. The process has been very different to my two previous novels. Writing *HellFire* came in clear distinct phases, each linked to a different writing product. Tiny short story, monologue, commissioned play—a dismal failure—then, out of the failure, 400 pages of handwritten text. Once I decided to commit to writing a novel instead of a play, it all went relatively smoothly. There were plenty of challenges, but generally, the process felt like a splurge. The words came out, unstoppable, then I took a few steps back and began the slower process of making them Better.

Writing my second novel was much more stop-and-startish. My first mistake was thinking I could grow it by using the *HellFire* model of expanding out from a small initial offering. I thought I knew what I was doing, and it took me five years to realise I didn't. Once I accepted I was failing and—after hearing Orna's lecture—understood why, I cut some material away. Then the process came, but slowly, in pieces, like a wave starting very small, very far out at sea. I worked on one strand, then another, then another, then brought it together to make it Better. Then, a few years later, I unwound the strands, reworked them, put them together, trying for even Better again.

My current novel began as a longish short-story in 2002. It was this I tried to grow into my second novel and it was that kernel—the initial short story—that I ended up cutting away from the rest in 2008. In 2011 I returned to it because I felt it still had something. It was then I made my second mistake: trying to sprout the kernel in lots of different directions, because that had worked for *Beautiful Pictures*. Three-and-a-half years later I finally accepted that wasn't working. By then I'd also started to question the wisdom of importing a process from a book that had—at that point—failed to sell. So I made a decision: I would focus in on one strand only. Two months later I'd got a 98 per cent terrible first draft done. Earlier this year I began reworking that.

Currently I've lots of words and a shape that resembles a beginning-middle-and-end, but it's not yet a novel. I'm going through it very slowly, making choices, undoing them, then remaking them. It doesn't feel splurgey like *HellFire* or tidal-wavish like *Beautiful Pictures*. It's more like I'm trying to whittle back a single small piece of wood to find what might be lurking inside. Whittle too little and I won't find it. Whittle too much and I'll be left with nothing. I'm very impatient. I want to keep pushing, keep going, finish the fucking thing. Every so often I flow for a couple of chapters. Then I get stuck and I hate myself and the book for a while. And then at some point I hear a voice in my head telling me *Go Back to the Beginning, Mia, there's something you've missed*. The voice is always right. There's always a moment where I haven't been clear, where I need to whittle some more.

The other week I talked to Ian Maleney about this piece and he mentioned delusion. Writing always involves trickery. I tend to fool myself into a situation where I have to keep going. Either I let the ideas build up, and put off the actual writing till I can't hold back and it comes out splurgey, like the runs, or else I write manically, pour a ton of words onto the page until I have so much it would be criminal not to do something with it. It's like swimming out into the sea, so far that turning back would be more dangerous than keeping going.

I've written a handout on what I've learnt from writing novels, and I'm happy to share it. But it's not a How To. I'm afraid you, like me, will need to find your own Via Negativa, fail on your own terms, fail again, and it'll never feel nice, and that's as it should be, because failure is painful, but if you keep failing, chances are you'll find your own brief, temporary fashion of coming up onto your toddler feet, before gravity pulls and you're down on the ground again, belly on the floor, palms kissing the earth, ready for the next doomed twist up.

The only tip I can safely give you is this: we're all going to die.

Practice

Career

In 2007 a lovely young man came to the door to sell me Sky TV. He asked me what I did and I said I wrote and he asked me if I'd anything published and I said yes, and showed him a copy of *HellFire*. Somehow the word 'career' came up. I felt very awkward. Oh no, I said, I wouldn't call it a career. The word seemed very businessy; conjuring up images of people in offices with briefcases. It also suggested a linear trajectory, with intention behind it. My experience of being a writer didn't feel linear at all, more like a series of choices to commit to—or abandon—various writing projects, in between doing lots of what my mum used to call 'other things'.

A couple of years later, when austerity hit, I and other writers were often asked to contribute letters petitioning against cuts in arts funding. In one, I found myself discussing how artists fall between several stools when it comes to their status within the economy. Writers' work gets called a host of names: vocation, entrepreneurship, even hobby. But none of these is fully accurate. Writing isn't a vocation like teaching or joining a religious order, because it serves the writer's needs as much, if not more than, those of the recipient community. It's not entrepreneurship, because businesspeople drop products the moment they stop making money. And it's not a hobby, though many writers work without guarantee of payment. Because of this confusing terminology, I argued, artists are subject to misconceptions—seen, as I've discussed earlier, as gifted child, sponging parasite or poverty-loving attic-dweller. As a consequence, they are vulnerable in a particular way to funding cuts and policy changes. If I don't know what I am within the socio-economic nexus of capitalism, how can I defend what I do?

Most of my files from 2009–2010 are on an old PC that I can't access anymore, so I don't have a copy of that letter. But I'm pretty sure I didn't use the word 'practice' in it. The first record I have of using that word to describe my work is in a CV and bursary application dated January 2011. Prior to that, I think I'd started using 'layered practice' as a way of making sense of the fact that I'd worked both as a theatre artist and a writer over the span of my working life.

I remember being thrown during a 2009 interview for a residency when Kenneth Redmond, the Dún Laoghaire-Rathdown Arts Officer, asked me to talk about my 'career'. Once again, the word seemed too big, too focused for where I was at. I didn't say that to Kenneth, or use the word 'practice' instead. I just went *ah, um*, then started telling a long and involved story about my transition from college student to baby revolutionary in Nicaragua. But I think during the residency, Kenneth himself—who'd trained as a fine art printmaker—may have guided me towards the term.

Practice. Once I found it, it felt right.

Deodorant

Practice is action. It suggests intention, preparation, a commitment to doing without being guaranteed—or having to manifest—a particular outcome. In this way, the term represents a shift away from capitalism's obsession with profit-making product. However, it's worth remembering that performers practise before they perform, and their practice usually results in performance—a product. Moreover, 'practice' has a seductive, ego-appealing connotation: Practice makes Perfect. This is codified memorably in Malcolm Gladwell's *Outliers*, his argument—recently disputed—that 10,000 hours of practising anything will make the practitioner excellent in their field.

The word 'practice' also has a certain socio-economic status, a precedent beyond artistic activity. Lawyers, accountants and health professionals all have 'practices'. Calling me a 'professional practising writer' bundles me in with this cohort. No longer do I fall between the stools of profit-hungry entrepreneur, saintly self-denying monk, or dilettantish hobbyist. 'Practice' says: You may think I'm a crazy off-the-wall artist who's crap at money, but actually I'm a professional, a grown-up like you; I'm one of those people that gets up in the morning. And this in itself makes the allocation of state, i.e. taxpayer, funding supports for artists more understandable, more legitimate and more palatable to those in power.

On this level, the term is suspect. It accepts rather than questions the existing social order. Professionals who have practices in health, law or finance usually also have skills and a university education, and come from privileged backgrounds. Their exchange value (manifested in their hourly rate) is relatively high. Most artists come from the bourgeoisie; not because artistic talent is the reserve of privilege, but because pursuing an artistic practice requires time, money, access to specialist knowledge and, crucially, insider information about power structures—including how to write Arts Council applications.

The word 'practice' brands writers as part of the texture of the bourgeoisie, separating them from unskilled or manual workers. Is it really a step away from the pyramid scheme of capitalism, or just—or also, perhaps?—a glossy way of masking the stink of shit flowing downwards?

Special to the power of minus-one.

Presence

A couple of years ago I had coffee with Sean O'Reilly and I told him about my first stab at a novel in 1990, and that I gave up on it when I felt it wasn't working. What would you tell that 23-year-old now? he asked. Keep going, I said.

In 1996, I gave up on a second novel-in-waiting, a *Game of Thrones*-type swords'n'sorcery wolfbuster. I'd finished a draft, my agent had sent it out, but it never got picked up. I didn't tell Sean about that book, but if I had, I'm sure he'd have asked me what I would say to that 29-year old now. Take a break, I'd say. And go back to it in time.

In 2011, somewhere in the middle of those twenty-plus rejections for *Beautiful Pictures*, I reached another crisis point. Nobody wanted my work, my exchange value was zilch, so what was the point in starting something new? I threw myself into a rake of projects that weren't 'proper' writing. I knew they were distractions. In the autumn, when the projects were over, I was back facing the crisis. What are you? said a friend. Um, a nice person, I said. No, she said. You're a writer. So write. Fuck off, I wanted to tell her, but in a shitty little hotel room in Cheltenham, between stints at a Christian arts festival, I forced myself to sit down and face the page. I rarely use the word scribbler, but that morning I did scribble. And afterwards I felt better.

It was then that I began to understand the inwards value, the Better value—not the exchange-value—of the term practice.

Practice is—like Lia's biog—something I do, not something I am. It means turning up and doing it, no matter what the outcome, no matter what does or doesn't happen. It is learning, it is unlearning. It is never, really, an arrival. Or if it is, each arrival is a new departure. It nurtures process and encompasses product, but it goes beyond both. It's bigger but less linear, and often less visible, than career. It's more selfish than vocation, it's less money-oriented than entrepreneurship, it's more serious than hobby. Ian Maleney uses the word 'discipline'. The closest 'practice' is to, perhaps, is 'amateur', but it's not amateurish. For me it'll do, for the moment.

I'm often asked by people for feedback on how they should complete a book or other Thing they're making. I usually ask them how long they've been working on it, how much time they intend to spend every week or every day going forward, and for how long. When they tell me their targets, I nearly always suggest they do less. If a writer is finding themselves stalled—and they're not contractually obliged to finish a work for a publisher, or, like me, contractually obliged to write because the tax-paying citizenship has invested in that—I don't suggest they make things worse by whipping themselves to work faster. You're stuck and feeling bad about it? Don't put in four hours a day. Put in one, or if that's too much, thirty minutes. Or twenty minutes, three times a week. Each time you turn up you build energy. It's the decision to be there that feeds the flame, not how long you stay once you've arrived.

To keep process moving, keep turning up, keep paying attention, keep practising. While our world may need more books, I don't think that's what it most needs, particularly not right now. Held hostage by profit and growth, our biosphere is under siege, and so is our collective humanity, our future. What I think is needed most in these scary, most interesting of times, is presence.

What is presence, but the clearest possible manifestation of love in action? If I love someone it's pointless telling them that but acting differently. If I love writing, then I must act as if I do. I must be in the presence of writing. I must write, even just for five minutes a day, even—especially—if I think it's shit. That's practice, and nobody can stop me—or you—doing that, not even the pyramid. Nobody except my—or your—self and, in the end, death.

from *The Book of Showers*

To praise
the rain

is to observe
how it slips us

through
the double words

it gives us,
how it allows

our mouths
to pronounce

the *fall*
in asphalt,

the *is*
in drizzle,

the *awe*
in squall.

Doireann Ní Ghríofa

WonderHouse (Some Assembly Required)

Stephen Walsh

Thank you on purchase of TinyMinds WonderHouse™! We hope it will bring you and your little explorers many hours of wonder and fun in years to come. Please follow these instructions <u>carefully</u> to ensure safe and pleasant use.

Step 1: Check you have all parts listed below.

Parts missing? Please call helpline number shown on page 28.

Twenty-eight pages. Check to see if some are in German/Chinese/etc. and can be skipped. Are not. Skip to page 28 to imagine/spoil ending. Pic of triumphantly assembled structure with stick-figure man, hand on hip, arm extended over creation, ready to commence many hours of fun and wonder complete with squeals of gratitude from daughter or similar loved one (not pictured).

Turn from glorious outcome back to step 1 reality. All parts checked and present. Parts many and various but trust all necessary and purpose will be revealed in due course. Let steps guide part Y (You). Separate into ordered alphabetised piles on carpet. Not all letters used. Be grateful 9 piles not 26 though. Create adequate space along with surely adequate two hours in Saturday afternoon. Now 4PM. To be assembled by 6PM and to be delivered to D for 7PM. Fun/wonder commences 7.15PM. Picture this: Oh wow this is the best thing ever etc. Oh no trouble no took less time than I thought you're very welcome etc. Picture this and press on.

Step 2: Have you all necessary tools? For also you will need:

1 Phillips head screwdriver

1 Hammer

2 People to support weight (NOTE: it is to assemble alone unsafe).

Check. Check. Not check. Just one person. Surely multitudes optional? One person (Y) was well able to drag box in here on own. Can't be heavier coming out. Have basic grasp of physics thanks! Cannot increase mass. Can only apply force and energy. So easily pulled in wrong distracting direction. Focus now.

Weird word order too, re assemble alone unsafe. Awkward translation from the original? Ominous/poetic tone is mildly disquieting. Also note step has defined people as tools.

Tools also present and necessary:

1 'Ambient Relaxation' Playlist (to put mind in calm receptive place during assembly).

1 Galway Hooker IPA 50cl 4.8% (for similar reasons. 1 only, as timely delivery top priority and assembly-transport-presentation arduous enough without additional snags).

Note 26 minutes gone and so far have just arranged various screws and planks in pleasing manner on carpet.

Step 3: Locate planks A. Insert short head screws J into planks A at intervals (see Fig 2). Be sure to insert screws into upper side.

Planks A located and upsided. Very compliant. Screws more inscrutable. Piles of unmarked screws of various dimensions. J = ? Does short head mean shortest screw? Or smallest head? Or only screws that will fit holes in planks A? Or all of these? Try a few screws. Most fit quite nicely into plank A. Cinderella moment this is not. But do not force. Know from experience that complexities arise if incorrect parts rammed into wrong place. Realise J was marked on one of many small plastic packages, but in haste to comply with step 1, Y removed all screws from packages and now no way to say which sprang from J-pack. This is what happens when instructions not followed. Pleasant-looking piles now swirling screwniverse of chaos. Enter realm of damned at 4.46PM. Open beer (1).

Unsurrender. Count holes in planks A. 24. Count number of screws in each pile. Only one of 24 identicals. Pride self on deductive abilities. J, meet A.

Kneel to urge ranks of J into planks of A. Some Js do not insert very neatly. Some gone in at quite an angle. Attempt to restore order but screwdriver is scratching and tearing at J heads. Partial misalignment = End of world? Surely a few loose connections won't cause WonderHouse to collapse trapping/ severely injuring occupants. Think of engineers whose similar nonchalant approach caused derailments, infernos, years of inquests. Overthinking. Future joy will not be structurally compromised by a few rogue screws.

Note steps 1 to 3 have consumed 58 minutes of allotted 120. Maybe disproportionately onerous? 4 to 27 possibly accelerated path to glory? Regard again page 28. See how stick-face smile imparts pride, relief, excellent parenting. Aspire towards. Open beer (2). Doesn't count as working it off anyway? Can always get taxi, might actually be better plan? Transport easier in a people carrier? Restart playlist as was not in calm receptive mood during step 3 and milky piano floaty voices and swishing wavy noises did not have intended effect.

Step 4: Simply Place Planks A onto base B as shown, taking care to align screws with holes in base. Do not Force.

Not simply. B rejects any suggestion of alignment with A. Bear mild-to-medium resentment towards breezy nature in which step is described belying feat of human endeavour within. *Simply Place Space Shuttle into Earth's Atmosphere as shown, taking care to align with landing site. Do not explode. Simply Place Flag onto Omaha Beach as shown, taking care to overwhelm enemy forces. Do not get massacred.* Some force clearly necessary, you tools. Align Planks A inelegantly/quite violently onto B. Cracking noise registered but no sign of exterior damage.

Stand up slowly, allowing flow of O Positive to return to compromised legs of Y. Push against teetering base B with beer empty (2). Go to kitchen and find remedy for unsteadiness. Assemble auxiliary screwdriver, carefully aligning Smirnoff, orange juice and ice. Liberally apply thoughts of other parts Y have forced into position but came unstuck. Specifically:

C: **Clara**, in Y's life and house until I am sorry but *we cannot be any more*

D: **Deana**, Clara's daughter and your wonder but not your daughter *is not yours* understand this please

E: **Elek**, recently added part not in original but his daughter *his* understand this and he is *still my husband* under Polish Law.

Place parts C and D on top of screwdriver and beer (3). Recall attempts to combine Y, C and D. All held together well enough at first (did not force) but Y did not see part E coming. Returning. Temporarily withdrawn E was not referred to in initial assembly, an oversight which is <u>sorry I am sorry wanted to tell you many times and could not but now he is and we must please</u>.

E has cleared customs. E now reconnected with C and D per original design, completing unit. Temporary part Y no longer required. Can now be removed / discarded. Y was briefly load bearing and <u>thankful yes grateful but understand this is how we must be</u>. CDE now freestanding unit functioning as intended <u>do not call</u>. If desired, or more accurately not, Y can be left in current position at right angle to WonderHouse, which at current work rate seems unlikely to be successfully delivered to D. Delivery to D is very much at Y's own risk. D is not original part or property of Y as was <u>clearly documented</u>. D's wonder is <u>not your concern anymore</u>. Manufacturer cannot be held responsible for consequences if WonderHouse used for unintended purposes.

Step 5: Now insert Hex Head Screws H into Base B in indicated holes (See Fig 3).

Prowl around B menacingly with screwdrivers (1 of each). No holes indicated. Fall to knees align eyes with plywood. Tilt base B upwards from carpet to examine. In looking upwards regard mantlepiece and photo of Y and D and pic of Y that D drew. Observe space next to fireplace where box of D's dolls / toys was. Colour of wallpaper unfaded in space glaring unoccupied at Y.

Turn back to base B to note that indicated holes are on underside. Fig 3 shows holes should be opposite of underside. Indicated holes in rows of inverted triangles, two eyes surprised mouths oh, oh, oh, did you think we were on the other side? Now why would we be there, Y? We're just little holes but if you ask us Y should have read ahead maybe? Now staring into the plywood face of complete restart. Somewhat uncarefully turn everything upside down. In doing so, observe how planks A swiftly untether themselves from their <u>at best temporary arrangement with B</u>. Consider fading light and disconnected WonderParts in floorpile at 6.28PM. Help needed. Helpline closes 5PM Saturdays. Unhelpful.

Stand up. Take measure of enemy. Take steps necessary.

Rip page 28 from instructions and set aside.

Compress rest of instructions into ball and apply to wall with force. Prepare screwdriver (3), adjusting ratio of V to OJ as required, tilting head to required angle. Remove shirt to regulate internal temperature. Kill Forest Rain sounds. Switch to Power Workout Playlist.

Unleash hell on Wonder.

Let anger, tools, beers, screws become one. Enter zone spoken of by top-performing athletes and musicians. This just wood from a tree and screws from a factory. This is not the undoing of Y this is just an obstacle life consists of these. Can cower in corner or push into them over them conquer them. Can be making of a person. Can look back and think was that really so overwhelming and anyway what kind of person surrenders just lies down says you win. No no no. Let these thoughts guide hands now.

At 7.34PM step back and consider wonder structure, supported by interior actual wall to which it is now affixed filling space where D's toys and D used to be. Side panels looking as if have weathered sitting room category 4 storm, several crooked and cracked. White decorative fencing F doing additional job of partially holding door in place. Roof slanting off sharply to left. Overall look is less WonderHouse more WitchHovel. WonderHouse now permanently inside your house. Not going anywhere. Has some sharp angles but could pass for page 28. Assume stickman pose and cast arm over. Say look what you made to assembled mass and nobody. You think I'm good for nothing? Well there was nothing here and now there is this and isn't that something?

Not yet it isn't. Parts missing. Parts that were holding Y up. Need to call.

Call helpline.

Text pic of WonderHouse (box not actual) to C. Call C. Explain to C that Y needs to connect with D, now, yes now. C refuses. Re-apply with a little more force, taking care not to break tenuous connection. Give me this. Today give me this.

Allow sufficient time for words to dry in air. Adding further words on top of first layer too quickly may cause cracking of C. Please, you cannot. I will let this just today but then no more please understand you cannot.

D is connected. Tell her Y has a great surprise. Tell her to look at pic just sent and say surprise happy birthday look what I made for you. Do you want to come over and see it? Why not today why not right now? No Y can't bring it to D's new house. Silly Y. I built your Wonder inside mine and now it's stuck. Need you here. D not speaking. Come over today? Would love to see you again, darling. Y missing parts so called helpline.

D disconnects. C returns to call. Tone appears darker than previous. If Y persists, C advises that an application of E may be required to remove unwanted stain. E can be dispatched at very short notice. I'm warning you. Please stop. For I do not know. What he will do.

Deal with Snag List.

Work on into darkness. Might have visitors one/several any minute. Need to deal with snags. Main snag being E. Can deal with E though. Said so on phone when he connected. Dealt with worse. Can't be harder to align and force into position than planks/screws. Come on over big man. I fucking dare you. As fixing WonderDoor (swinging loosely off hinges) picture E coming to real actual house door. Would rise to deal with exterior snag. E would be free-standing powerfully built unit. Would Invite E in. Well Elek, I wondered when we'd have a little chat. Would hold beer (6) behind back. Would extend arm over WonderHouse. Would ask E What do you think? Care to step inside? Then say with screwed up face say it like this You think you can just out of nowhere? And Turn my life upside down you fuck? and Miss them still love them you weren't here you can't just though these words loosely balanced and slipping off screwdriver beer base.

Enter WonderHouse.

Easier to work on Snags from inside. Lift door off as if inhuman strength. Actually hanging by one screw not difficult. Climb in on knees. Turn slowly onto back, bring head up, eyeballing screws jutting out at Y pointing mocking what are you doing in here. Tap against screws with beer empty (7). Picture tapping empty against E with force fully necessary. One good swing fixing him permanently in place fixing situation for good. Text C. I have rights this is your final warning please. Send. Tight in here but tight equals cosy yes? Some houses just too big and empty. This one full with people, person, one. Could take two. Could fit D in here too. Room for her. Picture as if camping in a forest, gentle rain falling, warm yellow glow safe in here. Could hang fairy lights as through loose panel in back can reach plug in house wall. Yes D we would be something in here. But wouldn't hold. D will keep growing. Picture her growing like sped-up nature video pushing Y aside bursting through roof climbing out and looking back at Y <u>oh, oh, oh did you think you could keep me in there? I'm off to Poznan with my actual dad, you tool</u>. Please. Please let me. Text unread. Knocking, who is how is, *there's no door*? Rise stand come in D finally come in E I'm ready breathe stand up get

Leave to dry for at least 12 hours.

A thin layer of O Positive now coating WonderHouse yellow plastic floor. Gauge quality of morning light coming in through now open-plan WonderRoof via real house window.

Recall final steps from previous evening.

Heard knocking on exterior door. Almost certain heard knocking. Raised to deal with/welcome/forgive depending on delivery. However was in awkward position inside WonderHouse long into night and internal balance/ awareness of surroundings not functioning correctly. Cracked head through roof. Looked into darkness before falling backwards aligning with several exposed J and H screws on base B.

Y in Y shape now, legs extended 45 degrees in opposite directions through where door should be. Roof plate L now red plastic blanket on chest. Fixed/ screwed in DeadWitch position.

Could safely exit WonderHouse now that all parts are where they belong. Remain instead in void while joints resettle. Could make call to helpline on page 28 on floor in O Positive pool. But aware now that warranty is voided. Helpline closed. Text unread.

Hold up page 28. Look in pale morning upon stickman, stickarm forever stretching towards impossible, stickface grimace fixed in everlasting anticipation of many unwondrous years to come.

FEATURED POET

Emer Lyons is a creative/critical PhD candidate in the
English programme at the University of Otago, Dunedin,
New Zealand and originally from Cork. Her poetry, fiction
and reviews have appeared in journals such as *Poetry Ireland
Review*, *The Tangerine*, *Headland*, *Mimicry*, *takahē*, *Southword*,
The Cardiff Review, *London Grip*, and *Queen Mob's Tea House*.

Theoretical Archaeology

Standing on the fire escape outside our apartment
I look through the window at you

I've spent all day thinking about getting knocked down
and about that one group archaeological trip I went on in university

underground, or we talked about going underground
into a tunnel carrying our pencils so we could crack them in half to ward off badgers

(apparently badgers are vicious creatures)

I was smoking at the time
I always loved smoking more than I loved myself

after that I went on trips alone, walking for miles into the countryside outside my town
trying not to get knocked down on blind corners while smoking

O, I did survey a castle with someone once
inside people smoked joints while we carried around clipboards and measuring tape

I shout all this through the window at you over the traffic noise
just because I'm telling you the truth doesn't make it real

on a scale

10.   my bones like tyres worn out
10.   tyres like bones empty
10.   empty like the cupboards after i broke all the crockery
10.   like the shards swelling in my palms
10.   like my palms rubbing our faces unrecognisable
10.   unrecognisable like a new continent i move to for myself
10.   myself in that continent like darkness
10.   like the darkness of two hands holding in the bright bright sun and everyone
           looking away

gremlins

the lights went out the window / we waited and waited / waited some more / we touched the quiet / touched the air / smiled a secret / the deep shadows / tonguing the only light / from a hundred miles away / like a long lime-green dress / or bright orange flowers / in tiny braids hanging limp / a fleck of silver in them / swaying a bright silver chain / like a dangling lightbulb charm /

the lights have gone /

this old punched life / time laughing / i really wanted you / so i was supposed to / worry about the time you won't miss / attract birds to the yard / wave good-bye / hope the lights never came back /

outside under a big oak tree / in the dark / radio waves / stood straight up / like they stuck their fingers in a light socket / snatching the far end of my eyes / shrill ringing on the ground / broken touches / i won't find out the truth / without you / inside echoed empty / nobody said a word / lips to the bottom / mumbled noise / peeked back around the corner / the lights flickered on / squealed alive / wiped slowly / everything / i should have said /

it's been a great day / and i am sorry / that we will only have time today / for tomorrow / i'd be happy to go on first / all by myself / last night probably just needs tuning /

but slumped / words remembered to sabotage / causing you to admit / that forever we slid down / that we needed the very edge / to get there /

careful / the way forward is / waiting / small wrong things / like fear / shriek what / nobody knows / for sure /

i photocopy vaginas

frame them
salon-style
pin ceramics to paper
watch the brand new moon
strongest of the year
makes me think
you are hiding things in buckets
the skin of my hands
becomes the skin of my feet
i belong in the hallway
with the parsley
making everything stick
i'm going to put a christmas tree
on the fire escape
blame it for my death
i think of all the people
i don't want to talk to
in the new year
i feel clean
forget that i never learnt
to wash myself
the pictures taken from the floor
have too soft edges
piece together like cake
i know you are out there
i say into the darkness
this time i'll see you coming

i want to live up a steel spiral staircase in montreal with you

where all the lesbians have
perfectly
cut
hair
the nape of your neck is beautiful
let me kiss the indents of your skeleton
whisper dirty things to you in serious situations
i'll get a job in forever 21
wear a leather crown
keep my back turned to the queue
attain a psychotic level of focus for folding
pretend i'm ten years younger than i am
we'll go to dance parties that start at 2am
fuck mindfulness
we'll smoke like everybody else
in that way they do there
all ooh la la
i'll hold your hand in the anarchist book shop
we'll stay awake listening to people on the street
make up whole lives for them
for ourselves
get a chihuahua
put it in a leather jacket
we'll live up those stairs
in a life
inaccessible

will the sun come out

i set traps
to catch things
(only) to free them

…

(i wish) i dare(d) to write
on unstable ground
to slash + burn

…

o(/my) lack
keep(s) me here w/flesh
+ words

wait(ing)

[   ]

                                        for each

                        slow

                                                tomorrow

Back When We Talked to the Dead

Mariana Enriquez

Translated from the Spanish by Megan McDowell

At that age there's music playing in your head all the time, as if a radio were transmitting from the nape of your neck, inside your skull. Then one day that music starts to grow softer, or it just stops. When that happens, you're no longer a teenager. But we weren't there yet, not even close, back when we talked to the dead. Back then, the music was at full blast and it sounded like Slayer, *Reign in Blood*.

We started with the ouija board at the Polack's house, locked in her room. We had to do it in secret because Mara, the Polack's sister, was afraid of ghosts and spirits. She was afraid of everything—man, she was a stupid little kid. And we had to do it during the day, because of the sister in question and because the Polack had a big family and they all went to bed early, and the whole ouija board thing didn't go over well with any of them because they were crazy Catholic, the kind who went to mass and prayed the rosary. The only cool one in that family was the Polack, and she had gotten her hands on a tremendous ouija board that came as a special offer with some supplements on magic, witchcraft, and inexplicable events that was called *The World of the Occult*; they sold them at newspaper kiosks and you could collect and bind them. Various issues had already had promotions with ouija boards, but they always ran out before any of us could save enough money to buy one. Until the Polack started to take the thing seriously and really tightened her belt, and then there we were with our lovely board, with its numbers and letters in grey, a red background, and some very satanic and mystical drawings all around the central circle.

It was always the five of us who met: me, Julita, Pinocchia (we called her that because she was hard and tough, the toughest in the whole school, not because she had a big nose), the Polack, and Nadia. All five of us smoked, and we left a terrible stench in the room the Polack shared with her sister. Not to mention it was winter when we started with the ouija board, and we couldn't even open the windows because we'd freeze our asses off.

And that was how the Polack's mother found us: shut in with all the smoke and the planchette going all kinds of crazy. She kicked us all out. I managed to salvage the board—it stayed with me after that—and Julita kept the planchette from breaking, which would have been a disaster for the poor Polack and her family, because the dead guy we were talking to right then seemed really evil. He'd even said he wasn't a dead spirit, but a fallen angel. Still, by that point we knew that spirits are some crafty liars and we didn't get scared anymore by their cheap tricks, like how they could guess birthdays or grandparents' last names. All five of us swore with blood—pricking our fingers with a needle—that we didn't move the planchette, and I believed it was true. I know I didn't. I never moved it, and I really believe my friends didn't either. It was always hard for the planchette to get moving at first, but once it picked up momentum it seemed like there was a magnet attaching it to our fingers. We barely even had to touch it, we never pushed it, we didn't even rest our fingers on it; it slid over the mystical drawings and the letters so fast that sometimes we didn't even have time to jot down the answers to the questions (one of us always took notes) in the special notebook we kept for just that purpose.

When the Polack's crazy mom caught us (and accused us of being Satanists, and whores, and called all our parents: it was a clusterfuck), we had to stop the game for a while, because it was hard to find another place where we could keep going. At my house, impossible: my mom was sick in those days and she didn't want anyone in the house; she could barely stand my grandmother and me, and she would straight up kill me if I brought home classmates. Julita's was no good because the apartment where she lived with her grandparents and her little brother only had one room, which they divided with a wardrobe to make two rooms, kind of. But it was just that space, no privacy at all, otherwise just the kitchen and bathroom, plus a little balcony full of aloe vera and crown of thorns plants—impossible any way you looked at it. Nadia's place was also impossible because it was in the slum: the other four of us didn't exactly live in fancy neighbourhoods, but no chance in hell would our parents let us spend the night in the slum, they would never go for that. We could have snuck around and done it without telling them, but the truth is we were also a little scared to go. Plus, Nadia didn't BS us: she told us it was really rough in the slum, and she wanted to get the hell out of there as soon as she could, because she'd had it with hearing the gunshots at night and the shouts of the drunk gauchos, and with people being too scared to come visit her.

So we were left with just Pinocchia's place. The only problem with her house was that it was really far away, we'd have to take two buses, plus convince our parents to let us go all the way out to east bumblefuck. But we managed it. Pinocchia's parents pretty much left her alone, so at her house there was no risk of getting kicked out with a lecture on God. And Pinocchia had her own room, because her siblings had already left home.

So finally, one summer night, all four of us got permission and went to Pinocchia's house. It was really far, her house was on a street that wasn't even paved, with a ditch running alongside it. It took us like two hours to get there. But when we did, we realised right away that it was the best idea in the world to make the trek all the way out there. Pinocchia's room was really big, with a double bed plus bunk beds: all five of us could sleep there, easy. It was an ugly house because it was still under construction: unpainted plaster, light bulbs hanging from ugly black cords, no lamps, bare cement floor, no tile or wood or anything. But it was really big, with a terrace and a barbecue pit, and it was much better than any of our houses. It sucked to live so far away, sure, but if it meant having a house like that—even an unfinished one—it was worth it. Out there, far from the centre of Buenos Aires, the night sky looked navy blue, there were fireflies, and the smell was different, like a mixture of burnt grass and river. Pinocchia's house had bars on all the windows, it's true, and it also had a giant black dog guarding it. I think it was a Rottweiler, and you couldn't play with it because it was so mean. Living far away was apparently a little dangerous, but Pinocchia never complained.

Maybe it was because the place was so different—because that night in Pinocchia's house we *did* feel different, with her parents listening to Los Redondos and drinking beer while the dog barked at shadows—that Julita got up the nerve to tell us exactly which dead people she wanted to talk to.

Julita wanted to talk to her mom and dad.

It was really good that Julita finally spoke up about her folks, because we could never bring ourselves to ask. At school people talked about it a lot, but no one ever said a thing to her face, and we jumped to her defence if anyone came out with any bullshit. The thing was that everyone knew Julita's parents hadn't died in any accident: Julita's folks had disappeared. They were disappeared. They'd been disappeared. We didn't really know the right way to say it. Julita said they'd been taken away, because that's how her grandparents talked. They'd been taken away, and luckily the kids had been left in the bedroom (no one had checked the bedroom, maybe: anyway, Julita and her brother didn't remember anything, not of that night or of their parents, either).

Julita wanted to find them with the board, or ask some other spirit if they'd seen them. She wanted to talk to them, and she also wanted to know where their bodies were. Because that question drove her grandparents crazy, she said; her grandma cried every day because she had nowhere to bring flowers to. But plus, Julita was really something else: she said that if we found the bodies, if the dead told us where they were and it turned out to be really real, we'd have to go on TV or to the newspapers, and we'd get famous and everyone in the world would love us.

To me, at least, Julita's cold blood seemed really harsh, but I thought whatever, let Julita do her thing. What we for sure had to start doing, she told us, was coming up with other disappeared people we knew, so they could help us. In a book on how to use the board, we'd read that it helped to concentrate on a dead person you knew, remember their smell, their clothes, their mannerisms, their hair colour, construct a mental image, and then it would be easier for the dead person to really come. Because sometimes a lot of false spirits would turn up and lie to you and go around and around in circles. It was hard to tell the difference.

The Polack said that her aunt's boyfriend was disappeared; he'd been taken during the World Cup. We were all surprised because the Polack's family was really uppity. She explained that they almost never talked about the subject, but her aunt had told her once in confidence, when she was a little drunk after a barbecue at her house. The men were getting all nostalgic about Kempes and the World Cup, and the aunt got pissed off, downed her red wine, and told the Polack all about her boyfriend and how scared she'd been. Nadia contributed a friend of her dad's who used to come for dinner on Sundays when she was little, and one day had just stopped coming. She hadn't really noticed that friend's absence, especially because he used to go to the field a lot with her dad, and they didn't take her to games. But her brothers noticed it more when he didn't come around, and they asked their old man, and the old man couldn't bring himself to lie to them and say they'd had a fight or something. He told the boys that the friend had been taken away, same thing Julita's grandparents said. Later, Nadia's brothers told her. At the time, neither the boys nor Nadia had any idea where he'd been taken, or if being taken away was common, or if it was good or bad. But now we all knew about those things, after we saw the movie *Night of the Pencils* (which made us bawl our eyes out; we rented it about once a month) and after the *Nunca más* report on the disappeared—which Pinocchia had brought from school, because in her house they let her read it. Plus there was all the stuff we read in magazines and saw on TV. I contributed with our neighbour in back, a guy who'd only lived there a short time, less than a year. He didn't go out much but we could see him moving around out the back windows, in his little back yard. I didn't remember him much, it was kind of like a dream, and it wasn't like he spent a lot of time in the yard. But one night they came for him, and my mom told everyone about it, and she said that thanks to that son of a bitch they could have easily taken us, too. Maybe because she repeated it so much, the thing with the neighbour stuck with me, and I couldn't relax until another family moved into that house and I knew he wasn't ever going to come back.

Pinocchia didn't have anyone to contribute, but we decided we had enough disappeared dead for our purposes. That night we played until four in the morning, and by then we were starting to yawn and our throats were getting scratchy from so much smoking, and the most fantastic thing of all was that Pinocchia's parents didn't even come knock on the door to send us to bed. I think—I'm not sure, because the ouija consumed my full attention—that they were watching TV or listening to music until dawn, too.

After that first night, we got permission to go to Pinocchia's house two more times that same month. It was incredible, but all our parents or guardians had talked on the phone with Pinocchia's parents, and for some reason the conversation left them totally reassured. But we had a different problem: we were having trouble talking to the particular dead people we wanted—that is, Julita's parents. We talked to some spirits, but they gave us the run around, they couldn't make up their minds yes or no, and they always stopped at the same place: they'd tell us where they'd been kidnapped, but then they wouldn't go any further, they couldn't tell us if they'd been killed there or if they'd been taken somewhere else. They'd talk in circles, and then they'd leave. It was frustrating. I think we talked to my neighbour, and he got as far as naming the detention centre Pozo de Arana, but then he left. It was him, for sure: he told us his name, we looked him up in *Nunca más*, and there he was, on the list. We were scared shitless: it was the first certified *for real* dead guy we'd talked to. But as for Julita's parents, nothing.

It was our fourth time at Pinocchia's when what happened happened. We'd managed to communicate with someone who knew the Polack's aunt's boyfriend; they'd gone to school together, he said. The dead guy we were talking to was named Andrés, and he told us he hadn't been taken away and he hadn't disappeared: he'd escaped on his own to Mexico, and he died there later in a car accident, totally unrelated. Well, this Andrés guy was cool, and we asked him why all the dead people took off as soon as we asked them where their bodies were. He told us that some of them left because they didn't know where they were, and they got nervous, uncomfortable. But others didn't answer because someone bothered them. One of us. We wanted to know why, and he told us he didn't know the reason, but that was the deal, one of us didn't belong.

Then, the spirit left.

We sat for a beat thinking about what he'd said, but we decided not to give it too much importance. At first, when we'd started playing with the board, we always asked the spirit that came if any of us bothered it. But then we stopped doing that because the spirits loved to run with the question, and they'd play with us. First they'd say Nadia, then they'd say no, everything was cool with Nadia, the one who bothered them was Julita, and they could keep us going all night, telling one of us to put our fingers on or off the planchette, or even to leave the room, because those fuckers would ask us for all kinds of things.

The episode with Andrés left enough of an impression, anyway, that we decided to go over the conversation in the notebook while we cracked open a beer. Then there was a knock at the door. It startled us a little, because Pinocchia's parents never bugged us.

'Who is it?' asked Pinocchia, and her voice came out a little shaky. We were all shitting ourselves a little, to tell the truth.

'It's Leo. Can I come in?'

'Hell yeah!' Pinocchia jumped up and opened the door. Leo was her older brother who lived downtown and only visited their parents on weekends, because he worked during the week. And he didn't even come every weekend, because sometimes he was too tired. We knew him because before, when we were little, first and second grade, sometimes he came to pick up Pinocchia at school when their parents couldn't make it. Then, when we were big enough, we started to take the bus. A shame, because then we stopped seeing Leo, who was really strong, a big dark guy with green eyes and a murderous face, to die for. And that night, at Pinocchia's house, he was hot as ever. We all sighed a little and tried to hide the board, just so he wouldn't think we were weird. But he didn't care.

'Playing ouija? That thing's fucked up, I'm scared of it,' he said. 'You girls have some balls.' And then he looked at his sister: 'Hey kiddo, can you help me unload some stuff from the truck? It's for the folks, but Mom already went to bed and Dad's back is hurting…'

'Aw, don't be a pain in the ass, it's really late!'

'Well, I could only make it out here just now, what can I say, the time got away from me. Come on, if I leave the stuff in the truck it could get lifted.'

Pinocchia gave a grudging okay and asked us to wait for her. We were left sitting on the floor around the board, talking in low voices about how cute Leo was, how he must be around twenty-three by now, that kind of thing.

Pinocchia was gone a long time, and we thought it was strange, so after half an hour Julita suggested she go see what was going on. Then everything happened really fast, almost at the same time. The planchette moved on its own. We'd never seen anything like it. All by itself, really, none of us had a finger on it, not even close. It moved and wrote really quickly, 'Ready'. Ready? Ready for what? Just then we heard a scream from the street, or from the front door—it was Pinocchia's voice. We went running out to see what was going on, and we found her in her mother's arms, crying, the two of them sitting on the sofa next to the phone table. Just then we didn't understand a thing, but later, when things calmed down a little—just a little—we more or less put it together.

Pinocchia had followed her brother down to the corner. She didn't understand why he'd left the truck there when there was plenty of room by the house, but he didn't answer any of her questions. He'd changed as soon as they left the house, he'd turned mean and wouldn't talk to her. When they got to the corner he told her to wait, and, according to Pinocchia, he disappeared. It was dark, so it could be that he walked a few steps away and she lost sight of him, but according to her he'd disappeared. She waited a while to see if he would come back, but since the truck wasn't there either, she got scared. She went back to the house and found her parents awake, in bed. She told them Leo had been there, that he'd been acting really weird, and that he'd asked her to help unload things from his truck. Her parents looked at her like she was crazy. 'Leo wasn't here, sweetie, what are you talking about? He has to work early tomorrow.' Pinocchia started trembling with fear and saying, 'It was Leo, it was Leo,' and then her dad got all worked up, and shouted at her and asked if she was high or what. Her mom was calmer, and she said: 'Listen, let's call Leo at home. He's probably asleep, but we'll wake him up.' She was doubting a little now too, because she could tell that Pinocchia was really positive and really upset. She called, and after a long time Leo answered, cursing, because he'd been fast asleep. Their mom told him, 'I'll explain later,' or something like that, and she started to soothe Pinocchia, who was having a terrible meltdown.

They even called an ambulance, because Pinocchia couldn't stop screaming that 'the thing' had touched her, an arm around the shoulders, in a sort of hug that had made her feel more cold than warm, and that it had come for her because she was 'the one who bothered them'.

Julita whispered into my ear, 'It's because she didn't have anyone disappear.' I told her to shut her mouth—poor Pinocchia. I was really scared, too. If it wasn't Leo, who was it? Because that person who'd come to get Pinocchia looked exactly like her brother, he was like an identical twin, and she hadn't doubted for a second either. Who was it? I didn't want to remember his eyes. And I didn't want to play with the ouija board ever again, let me tell you, or even go back to Pinocchia's house at all.

Our little group never got together again. Pinocchia was hit really hard, and her parents blamed us—her poor parents, they had to blame someone. They said we'd played a mean prank on her, and it was our fault she went a little crazy after that. But we all knew they were wrong; we knew the spirits had come to get her because, as the dead guy Andrés told us, one of us bothered them, and it was her. And just like that, the time when we talked to the dead came to an end.

Correspondences

Calling for an end to direct provision

Hina Khan

Foreword | Jessica Traynor

A few years ago, I sat at the dinner table in my parents' house, asking my dad, a Finglas native born in the 1950s, what he had known as a child about the industrial school at Artane. He recalled that there was almost a glamour around the boys, but a dangerous glamour—they were separated from society for some reason that wasn't clear. But it had something to do with difference, with badness.

I wondered what my own children might ask me about when they are old enough to start tangling with history, society, and what is silenced.

My father grew up in a society indoctrinated by a conjoined church and state into believing that mass incarceration was for the betterment of society. I grew up in the 1980s and 90s, when old certainties were slowly, grindingly being eroded and in some wonderful cases, being swept away.

And yet. In 2000, direct provision was introduced as a temporary measure. Almost twenty years later, this carceral system is still in place. As a citizen of this state, how do I explain this? How will I explain my silence to my children?

During Field Day's Right to Have Rights lecture series in 2017, I was invited by Stephen Rea to read alongside alongside writers and activists currently in direct provision. The idea for *Correspondences* was born there, and grew through discussion with activists and artists, all of whom gave sage advice. We were keen not to ghettoise work in an ephemeral anthology that would create short term engagement with artists and writers in direct provision, and short term results. We wanted to pair artists and writers in the system with Irish writers for mentorship opportunities, in the hope that these working relationships and friendships would outlast the process of the anthology itself. We wanted to benefit a charity run by and for applicants for international protection, and so we have chosen MASI as the beneficiary of the proceeds.

Mostly, our hope for the project now is that it will foster empathy, connections, and understanding, between a misunderstood and sometimes demonised community made up of diverse people with complex lives, and the people who have the privilege to live in the Irish state without fear, without suspicion, and without prejudice.

Here, we are publishing a small selection of the stories, poems and art by artists in direct provision that feature, alongside work by Irish writers, in *Correspondences*. So this is where the story begins. We hope you'll buy the book to find out how it ends.

They will come for you

Remember when they come for you
day or more likely night
remember
electric light on the stairs or maybe dark
remember when they come for you
half-finished lemon tea
remember when they come for you
only words smile or silence
when they come for you
when they come for you
they won't remove their leather boots
they won't look at the black and white picture
hanging on the wall
where you are smiling to your aunt
totally happy
ten months old
they will never shrink their heart
when they come for you
remember that mild morning
on the Onega lake
when the water was extremely cold
and extremely inviting
the clearest water you've ever seen
remember that kiss that you give to your best friend
to that tall boy from your school
so good at chemistry
to lose him forever
to keep him forever
in your tired chest
you were woven of these smallest details
when they came for you

Evgeny Shtorn

I had to keep on | Anonymous

As narrated by an Afghan man to Dr Natasha Remoundou in late April 2019.

That morning the Taliban broke into our house. They beat me and my mother so bad and locked us in a bedroom. My father was not at home as he was in the army. We stayed in the room locked and terrified until night fell and then one of the Taliban unlocked the door and I escaped with my mother. I was so badly injured that I had to go to the hospital. I thought my injuries were not that serious but when I went to the hospital I got stitches on my head. I was only 16 years old. Then my mother talked to someone and I escaped the country by car. The Afghan driver was unknown to me and he drove me to Pakistan. My mother had arranged everything so that I would be saved. My mother stayed behind. They killed her. Still to this day, I do not know where my father is. In Pakistan, I had an aunt who lived there with her family. She is my mother's sister. When I went to Pakistan I stayed in the hospital for three weeks because I was bleeding on my head. Then my aunt told me that I had to leave the country. I was posing a threat to her own family and her husband was not happy with me staying with them. They were afraid that they would be in trouble as the Taliban were looking for me.

I crossed the borders again with a group of people. My aunt and her husband found people to take me out of the country. So I left Pakistan and crossed again the borders with a group of other people and reached Iran. I stayed there for a year. It was very tough there. I did not know anyone there and it was very difficult my time there. I met a few Afghan people—most of them illegal—who gave me a place to stay and I worked for a year sewing clothes for very little money. I could not complain because I was illegally in the country and if I got caught they would deport me to Syria. Because I had no legal documents, there were only two options available for me if

I got caught: either to go join the army and fight in Syria in the war or go back to my country Afghanistan. I have a lot of friends who were coerced and recruited to become Hazara (Shi'a) fighters. I did not want to do this.

From Iran I walked with a group of people through the mountains to Turkey and from there we took a boat to Mytilini, an island in Greece. We tried a few times to reach the shore. I saw people drowning. From the fifty people we set off with only fifteen of us made it to Mytilini. I don't know how to swim. Even people wearing vests drowned.

In Mytilini, twenty or thirty of us got arrested by the police and we were put into jail for six to seven months. But I was lucky. You can stay for up to two years in prison for no reason. Just for crossing the borders. Just because you are a refugee. After I was released from prison I was given a document stating that I had one month to leave the country. If within this month you fail to do so, they put you back in prison or they deport you back to your country of origin. I was broke and knew no one there. It was difficult to leave Greece. From Mytilini, I borrowed money and took a ferry to Piraeus. Once I arrived in Athens I had no connections. If you don't make friends you have problems. And that is the same everywhere. Greece was a beautiful country, but I didn't like it there. There was a lot of racism. A large group of people, around fifty of them, would attack you in squares wearing black T-shirts and balaclavas. This never happened to me but to my friend. I never went out at night-time. I used to live in the city centre, in Acharnon, near a church. I made a friend who helped me when I was there. But after a month I had to leave Greece, so I left Athens and went to Thessaloniki, and from there I started walking. It was winter time.

There was no snow, but it was freezing cold and it rained heavily. My feet were soaked and cold. My clothes were wet from the constant rain. I was walking for hours when I saw a bridge and a railway line on a rocky area. There were huge rocks around me. My feet were swollen and bleeding. I went under the bridge. All my clothes were soaked wet but I was carrying a sleeping bag in my backpack. I had no other choice but to sleep there as I was exhausted. I took all my clothes off and remained naked in that foreign landscape in the cold and got in my sleeping bag. Only a few minutes passed when I started shivering from the freezing cold. My body could not stop shaking. My eyelids were closing. One thing kept coming to my mind: that if I allowed myself to fall sleep I would die. I said, No. You have to wake up. I got out of my sleeping bag, put my wet, cold clothes back on and said to myself that I had to keep on walking. I walked for three more kilometres. There was no other option or choice. I had to walk. I found a police station and wanted to be caught and sent back. Then I would have ten days to cross the border again. Indeed, they sent me back.

Ten days later I prepared myself again for crossing the Greek borders. With new clothes, new shoes, a new bag. I decided to take the same route. The way I knew. Following the railways. Only this time I was not on my own. I was part of a group of refugees all of us crossing the borders out of Greece together. We were strangers but all there for a common journey. That journey was not easier the second time around. A father and a son were crushed by a train inside a tunnel. I heard their cries that last moment. It was on the border with Macedonia. When you were in a train tunnel, you had to position your body in a certain way to avoid being crushed by the train.

The rest of us carried on. We reached Kosovo and then Serbia. In Macedonia, Albanians robbed us. They took our mobile phones, our clothes, our shoes, watches, wallets. Then we crossed to Serbia. Then we reached Hungary. There it was so bad: Hungarian police were so racist. I had no clothes. I found a pair of girls' flip-flops in the garbage. They were very small on my feet but had to wear them. The Hungarian police gave us nothing. I was wearing a woman's leggings. I found clothes and shoes on the street. I had no other choice. We ate what we found from our friends. No locals ever offered us food. We carried no weapons with us. Then we went to the prison in Hungary on the borders of the country. I could not walk any more as I had severe blisters. I stayed in a camp for two weeks waiting for my feet to heal. From there we had to keep walking. We reached France. We found ourselves in the Calais refugee camp. From there we hid inside trucks for days to reach Ireland. I got inside the top of a truck. In some trucks there could be as many as ten people hiding. They caught me a few times hiding in trucks. They start spraying and refugees come out. From Calais I reached finally Dublin after a twenty-hour trip. From there I was put in direct provision. And here I am.

Mother Tongue

My language is as thick as my mother's
it was passed down to me like the curves
of my sharp Xs and j-like expressions on Ys
now carried over the seas slowly forgetting expressions
my tongue is as sharp as a two-edged sword
it can slice you to bits without you even noticing the brutal I—
barbeque that I slay when it's meant to be BBQ
my language is the diviner of roads
knocking on the knock knock beetle
as I crack open the clicks on my tongue
Irqika lendlela luqoqothwane
I was bred by deep souls of culture
so engraved in my blood refusing to deteriorate
like my name uMinenhle
the beautiful afternoon that people turn down
because of their ungifted unsharp tongues
they don't know that I climb up over mountains as spirits flow through my tongue
I am a knock knock beetle
I am after all my mother's daughter
the road's imigwaqo
the traffic light's robots
the flows of my qa qe qi qo qus
are the chewings of xhaku xhaku
and the spitting out of seeds from people
undeserving of my mother tongue?

Mimmie Malaba

What's in a Name? | Rehan Ali

It's the wind. No more Samurai Jack. Only pixels of black and white, dancing in a relentless pattern on the screen. No more cartoons. What to do now? Where to go? Oh, it will be another boring summer day in Bridgewater House.

The subdued light from the clouded sky glows through the cracked glass. Better than no light. The window opens with a struggle. A fresh breeze creeps in. My hand reaches out at the wall that swarms with rusted satellites. A collection of black and bronze unblinking eyes. I feel the rough mesh with my fingertips. Three storeys high, I pull it towards me, trying not to look down. It has to face eastwards. The perfect angle. Did it work? A quick twist of my neck towards the buzzing screen says no. Hmm... maybe if I do this? No, still not working. But the view isn't all bad, I guess. I can see the New Bridge. Traffic lights. Cars. Trucks. Bikes. And people. But I'm looking from underneath, half veiled and half breathing. I am under.

'How many times do I have to tell you?' she walked in yelling.

I had been told before of the dangers of falling. Although landing was really the dangerous part. I pulled away with a sigh; the window closed off the world once more.

'But what about my cartoons?' After all, every ten-year-old child watches cartoons. I couldn't be that different.

'You will have to do something else,' she said.

But what? I guess I could roam the hostel, see what I could find. Perhaps a friend.

Best friends, I had so many. Reza from Iran, Ose from Nigeria, Roman from Russia, Chechnya, China, Kenya, Iraq. This was the brief window of time where I had none. They would come and go, I would remain. Ten years. Solitude, confined. I was part of the world and yet not. Wandering from floor to floor. How many paintings on the walls? Twenty-eight, for sure. One had a gold frame, and a bowl placed by the edge, like me on the windowsill. I'd become familiar with the edge, as had my mother.

She wanted to give us the open sky and unfolded sea. To blaze a trail so we could succeed. The mail that has been left for her has different intentions. I saw it earlier, by her bedside. Brown and large. I've always known, I guess, that there was something to be feared. I can feel it coming. Although my eyes are shut tight by the force of childhood, I can still sense it. Yes, it's here. And much like the weather, she can't quite keep it together. She's been losing sleep and I've been keeping myself awake. I can sense her thoughts: Can I make it before I lose my mind? Who chooses what stays and what fades away? We need a revelation. It's time to pray. The old remedy. But it's a prayer I can't complete tonight. Where do we go from here? Self-serving prayers only go so far.

'Why do you live there?' 'What is it?'
    Questions I've heard growing up. We're sewn into the landscape, can't you see? How can we return now? The pressure of heavy choices. You want to get it, right? But you don't understand the violence of a choice. And all we are, are choices, not a thousand different faces. My history is etched into documents. My life simplified into black and white. It isn't enough? How long before I am released from behind these walls? I want my future. You can make do with my past. I need the day, I'm growing tired of this night.
    But still I remain nameless. Like the others.
    'What's in a name?' you ask. I wish to be named.
    Call me whatever you want. Anything you want. Tell me what you want me to be. As long as freedom accompanies your calls. This place is a house, but this soil is a home. And it is where we need to exist. We can't leave now. And go where? Land over land, blood over sand. What a place to come from. Will we really no longer be able to stay? Much like the river Suir under the New Bridge, my mind runs free. But will it drown me? A fantasy of a world not overgrown, a world of compassion and promise remains fantasy after all. Will we drown?

But there's plutonium in our veins. Don't come too close, we might explode. A volatile group. Kept away, but barely atoms apart. Our ambition: a complex equation. Our hope: a catalyst. There's nothing quite like this. Our love: the purest element. Can you feel it? Our half-life: a quarter of yours. Oxidised by a stranger air. Will we always be afraid? Or is it we who are feared? Risk it all for one bright spark. Let our chemicals spill. Let our fumes dissolve. Born out of the earth, soil darker than yours. Breaking down again, although the barriers are lasting. And you simply can't get enough. More, more, more, just not enough.

But this is a good place to fall. A good place to end. Or maybe, just maybe, a place to begin. What do I choose? At the end of the road, when there's no more hope. I choose me. I choose us. I am young. So let us fall, but let us restart.

905976-14 | Donnah Vuma

905976-14: the number that identifies me and my three children for the five years that we have been resident in Ireland. From the moment we landed in Dublin and declared that we were seeking international protection, all the documents that identify us as individuals were taken away from us and replaced with a blue ID card. This card bears an identification number and states in bold red letters that it is not an identity card. I knew from that moment that we had become a statistic, another number!

*

Seeking asylum is not a crime; it is a fundamental human right that should be safeguarded by all nations. Ireland is a signatory to the Geneva Convention and is therefore obligated to uphold that right. It is extremely unfortunate that seeking protection and safety comes at the price of one's freedom. Direct provision as a system does not allow you to heal, to forget and to move on with your life. It is impossible to go through the day without reliving your past traumas. You live in constant fear of being called into interview and having forgotten any detail about when and where a particular incident occurred. Should you forget, you are deemed to be 'inconsistent' and fabricating your fear, therefore meaning that your claim for protection is bogus. Instead, the direct provision system in Ireland (and indeed the international protection system) is extremely cruel, discriminatory, racist and violates the most basic human rights. It is a profit-making system that strives on the misery of vulnerable human beings; it is a system that benefits private contractors to the tune of multi-millions every year. No one should ever be allowed to benefit financially from the vulnerability of other people. As an asylum seeker in Ireland you are forced to live in limbo and in forced poverty, due to state-imposed limitations and discrimination with no rights to basics such as the right to work and the right to education.

*

When people leave their home countries to seek asylum, driven out by unbearable situations that pose a danger to their lives, they leave behind most of their material possessions. But there are certain things that they cannot and do not leave behind, things such as education, skills, expertise, dreams and ambitions for themselves and their children. People flee with the hope that they will be able to start or continue living a meaningful life, as with any individual in a 'normal' situation. We are forced to live in isolated centres that are segregated from local communities. We are forced to raise families on a meagre income of €38.80 a week.

In 2018, 'our' government opted into the EU Directive that brought Ireland in line with many EU member states, but evidently did very little to provide a meaningful right to work for International Protection applicants. When Ireland opted into the EU Directive on Reception Conditions, the Department of Justice said that some 3000 people would qualify for the permit, which the department considers to be generous. But only 330 people have actually secured work with the new permit out of 1521 permits issued to people living in direct provision.

The difficulty with the permit is that it is granted on a piece of paper when other non-EU/EEA workers in Ireland have a GNIB or Irish Residency Permit Card. As such, many employers do not know much about it and applicants have to explain it themselves to potential employers. The second problem with it is that the permit is valid for six months and is renewable. But the uncertainty over renewal and it being valid for six months already limits employment to short-term, usually low-paying contracts. Then, once a person has been working for at least twelve weeks, they must pay to live in direct provision or find alternative accommodation. It is already difficult enough for people who have been granted protection to leave direct provision, with some taking six to eighteen months to find accommodation. Thus, the prospect of paying to live in direct provision is very real.

The other major problem with the permit is that it's only issued to people who have been waiting for a first-instance decision for at least nine months. It means that for nine months a person will not be allowed to work. And those who have been in the system longer, mainly in the Appeals stage of the application process, are disqualified from working, which increases the pool of people who are working in slave-like conditions for as little as €50 per week because they are desperate to provide for their needs. If €50 per week means avoiding having to ask a contractor appointed by the government for a slice of bread or cup of coffee, then it is worth it for many people in the system. Unfortunately, restrictions on work rights has normalised these conditions.

*

We cannot talk about direct provision and its violation of human rights without addressing the violations of the rights of the child. This is an issue of major concern. The 2000+ children living in direct provision are not entitled to any social welfare benefits including the child benefit allowance that is given to Irish national children and children of Non-EU citizens legally working in the state. Children also have the right to a loving and nurturing environment; direct provision is not a loving and nurturing environment. On the contrary, it is often a hostile space that must be shared with strangers. It is a space where children are exposed to inappropriate behaviours, nudity, language and conversations. There is no space for physical play or mental stimulation required by a developing child. Children are forced to follow a monotonous routine, everything is done the exact way it was done the day before.

*

All children have the right to health care and nutrition, but children living in direct provision go for years without knowing the taste of their own mother's cooking. The centres often don't have self-catering facilities, meals are on a two-day rotation menu served at specific times three times a day. There is no special menu for children to ensure that the dietary needs of a developing child are met or to ensure that the food is specifically prepared for their young palates, and this often leads to numerous health problems. Those children must go to school and interact with many children whose parents are able to provide for their needs. Children in direct provision have their school lunches prepared by a contractor that is appointed by the government. The contractor decides what their school lunch will be.

*

There are other simple things that can foster a childhood worth remembering, like going on holiday with the family or going out to the movies with friends from school. Teens in direct provision are robbed of ordinary teen experiences and have the added stress of knowing that no matter how well they do in school, they cannot access third-level education unless they are lucky enough to get a scholarship. Children have the right to equal opportunity and quality education; this is not a reality for children living in direct provision. Though the government introduced a higher education pilot support scheme, part of the qualifying criteria is that students completing the Leaving Cert and looking to progress onto higher or post-Leaving cert courses should have been a minimum of five years in the Irish education system as of 31 August 2017, and have been an applicant for protection or leave to remain for a combined period of five years, and not pending a deportation order. If a deportation order has been issued, that child is automatically disqualified from availing of the scheme.

*

The obvious impact of not being allowed to work or access further education, as well as living in limbo with the threat of deportation and everything that comes with direct provision, is huge on the mental health of a person. You can see the effects manifest in many ways; drug and alcohol addiction, gambling addiction and the recent increase in suicide and suicide attempts. People who are in the asylum process had jobs in their countries and suddenly they are not able to work and provide for their needs or for the needs of their loved ones. These are people who have already lost so much of what it means to live a normal life in their countries, and yet their supposed place of sanctuary robs them of that ability to provide for themselves. Both parents and children in direct provision experience mental health problems because of the State-sanctioned poverty they live in.

*

The restrictions on working rights and education rights create communities from asylum and refugee backgrounds that have difficulty entering the labour market once they are eventually granted some form of protection. Most people will have spent a long time without a real right to work and thus have a huge gap in their CVs. And other barriers like language, foreign qualifications and discrimination against Africans in the workplace contribute to the difficulty of integration for people with an asylum background. People who were once able to provide for their needs are suddenly stripped of that right and must depend on the State's cruel system. Getting a simple slice of bread or trip to the dentist to clean teeth becomes a herculean task, all because the government has decided that asylum seekers must live in poverty while their applications are pending.

*

We need to realise that children are like sponges: they watch and absorb everything we do as adults, the things we pay attention to and those that we don't. The situation created by the direct provision system is troubling and dangerous. We are raising the future residents of Irish society in a place that is teaching them that it is acceptable to be dependent and helpless and that it is acceptable to be able to live on charitable handouts way below the poverty line. We are showing our children that a living allowance increase from €19.10 to €38.80 is something worth celebrating. Can you then imagine what happens when you move that individual from €38.80 a week to €180 per week?

*

Institutionalising and warehousing human beings is unacceptable and mother to a list of endless problems. Nobody should ever be placed in a situation where they feel like they are less than human. Seeking asylum is not a crime; it is a human right that we are all entitled to. It is unacceptable and unforgivable that children are being forced to grow up in these conditions. The system of direct provision needs to be abolished immediately.

Síscéal

Chuir an Chailleach Ghlic an gheal
Ina dubh ar Kathmandu, d'iompaigh
An dealán ina chith mharfach, chas
Deiseal ina thuathal, thiontaigh
An grá ina ghruaim, agus leath
Brat bréagach ar lomchlár na fírinne.

Ach *bistari, bistari*. Fillfidh an feall
Ar an gCailleach Ghlic, scaipfear
Doircheacht an cheo nimhe a d'ardaigh sí,
Scaoilfear an ceangal a shnaidhm sí
Ar chúig caol na fírinne, agus beidh
An dubh ina gheal ar Kathmandu arís.

Paddy Bushe

Bistari, bistari: 'tóg breá bog é/take your time' sa Neipeailis.

Fairytale

The Sly Old Witch beguiled the light
Of Kathmandu towards dark, concocted
Poisonous rain from sunshine, wrenched
The sun itself from its course, twisted
Love into its own antithesis, and spread
A black cloak of deception over the streets.

But *bistari, bistari*. Betrayal will ineluctably
Come slinking back around the Sly Witch,
The foul mist she conjured will be dissipated,
That web of malevolence wherein she bound
The truth will loosen, and dark will turn
Towards the light once more in Kathmandu.

—an file é féin a d'aistrigh.

The Roundabout

Stand on the platform
and pass into the suburbs
the harmonious lights
of streets and grids
neighbours curled up by electric fences
coats caught on razor wire
for nothing at all
there there
in the distance
are the shopping centres
and the reptilian aspect of the overpass
Shaking off sirens
our bird brains and rainbows
view the airport rising
from the ground-flow
the electricity of millions
of hangars hiding Saudi jets
and crates of technologies
we don't know we need yet
from the enterprise zone
in emptied space near Saigon
The newspaper boy is crying his eyes out
on a north Dublin roundabout
hundreds are dead in the Congo
there was a girl he knew from home
he thinks she left with some Ukrainians
one day they came
in long leather coats and caps
who dresses like that?
she nodded
and left
who cares
his eyes all red on the roundabout
people die everyday in the Congo
isn't that what Conrad was getting at?
with his *Heart of Darkness*
and *Apocalypse Now*
yes I know
Some Saudis flew into a building
but that was years ago
I know Americans who still won't get on a plane

but we all know the chances
the statistical risk and
all that they say about being hit by a bus or
        struck by lightning
we still go out on the streets
take boats and trains underground
hours after bombings
there
there in the distance is the overpass
glistening with rainbows and carbon
we can see everything from here
between the balance of apartment blocks
and leftover fields
hedgehogs crying
here we are
here we are
and teenagers texting
leave us alone
we know
you are an engine of change
and embrace the challenge
you are passionate but manage it
and we are all connected
I stand on the platform
shafts of light in place of elevator cables
shelters barricaded
by the homeless and underage
(they drink the same brands
of beer and vodka)
the spirits now live in the suburbs
they are working on their image
their platform
leads to ticket checkers at tiny gates
hopeless rusted walkways
and lights unknown
drag across the bay
wailing wailing wailing
Who calls at this hour?
I find myself looking at the sky
I clear my head of words like blue

Alan Jude Moore

The State of the Place

'A sea of jade and muscatel.' You had me at 'gun-metal.'
Percussive words, the 'flying taps,' the birds, their 'hurl and gliding,'
'inviolate curve,' carnal or incarnate slip between wind and wing:
The difference between falcon, gull, or even crow being
so much less than the difference between land and air.

On YouTube, an offscreen scuffle then, sudden occupation
of a room like any room except for that guitar—
last night's empty glass, and is that takeaway, framed picture
of a duck or pelican or other made-up bird, an anorak,
your Dublin accent tangling with this knotted and embossed
unlikely language, reading 'Glassblower' as if surprised
it's not a letter from the ESB. That it is not.

'The green tips burst' and old trees feel *as if*
'My heart in hiding / stirred,' wanting to know and unexpectedly,
wanting to be known. 'That's the Objective Correlative,' as Dugan says,
'between us poets, love.'

Mairéad Byrne

Recordar, Mas o Menos

Paul Lewis

Barcelona: *verano* **2002**

With Dot and many friends. No affinity with, no reference for, Spain. Barcelona is just a big, sunny city by the sea, away from home. I remember: the hills, the sea, terracotta Sagrada Familia unmoored in sky-blue, aristocratic Passeig de Gràcia, heat, rubbish, multitudes of people, the city overwhelming me, block after block, never stopping. Remember: dreadlocked drummers and *capoeiristas*, clouds of dust in Parc de la Ciutadella, pink tourists, yellow rice, purple sangria and golden beer on La Rambla. Old fishwives smoking, sharpening curved bloodied cleavers, sheen of tuna skin in la Boqueria's musty light. Birds in cages, *putas'* heels clip-clopping, *la policía*, krustypunks, dogs on strings, alms for the grotesquely deformed. A tragic mime drinks wine outside a ramshackle bodega, the Raval's freakshow madams, serviced a million sailors, outside doors that lead upstairs. Hustlers. ¡*Ladrones!* Bewildered, hash-stoned, half-drunk, I traipse from *pico* uptown through broadspaced industrial *barrios*, enormous traffic-heaving *rondas* then streets, winding, cobbled, down-at-heel, past the Miró, the port, superyachts, and table-clothed seafood restaurants, into Barceloneta, narrow, straight, crustaceous, cool. Clean, laundry hanging, icons behind screens, sunglassed party animals, the syrupy Mediterranean seeping into hot gritty sand.

Back to Ireland. Broken. Flat broke. Find apprenticeship in kitchen. Me and Dot break up.

Madrid y Granada: *marzo* **2004**

Madrid airport. Bombwrought car park through train window. Visiting Dot, now studying in Madrid. Kevin will join after a few days. Did I spend the day in el Prado? Velazquezes, El Grecos, Picassos? Could have been another time. Definitely spent the day in the quietness, the immensity, the glare of the city; so subdued, griefstricken. Arrive in Alcalá, where Dot lives, where the other bomb went off. It's uncomfortable. Someone makes dumplings, at once pleasant and unpleasant. Decide with Dot and her German flatmate to visit friends in Granada. Be back in time for Kevin's arrival. Out of the metropolis, over desert motorway, southbound. Miles of oranges, olives, *gasolineras*. Granada appears. Oasis-like.

Saint Patrick's Day. Visit Alhambra. Everyone's out that night. Dot out of sorts. Go back to apartment. She goes to bed at end of hall. Worried, I try to stay awake. Woken by drunken German coming back. Wants me to cook with him. Bad feeling. Go check. Dot is gone.

German flatmate leaves. Kevin comes to Granada. Talk with Dot's family in Cork and boyfriend in Málaga. Police find her. After an ordeal, but safe. Remember: Granada's otherworldliness, people's kindnesses, searching for Dot in park named after Lorca, sitting on a plaza with Kevin, drinking and laughing with relief. Dot spends few days drugged in horror psychiatric ward. Kevin must go home. Dot's boyfriend arrives, brings us to Málaga airport. Dot drugged heavily for flight. Airport police. Interrogation. I have a letter from the hospital.

País Vasco y Barcelona: *verano* 2005

A la playa. Vermut. Pintxo de tortilla con cerveza. Copa de tinto. ¡Puplo! ¡Sepia! ¡Bocadillo de calamares! ¡Cortados! ¡Helado de pistachio! ¡Golfo de Vizcaya, que azul!
Stay in Rick's garage, above Parc Güell. Working-class homes, *club de petancas*, villas of the rich, squats, howling wildcats. This is dusty Carmello. Barcelona, but apart. Days in the dusty garden, overlooking. Wander the city to one of its beaches. Go to clubs and parties all night with Rick. Spend last of my money eating at Santa Maria, a place I have read about. Go back home. Get job.

Mallorca y Barcelona. *octubre* 2007

Make pilot cookery show with Frank. Fishing boats, prawns, squid, hake, *paella* in the plaza, olive oil. Under the sun in orange and olive groves. *Carajillos de coñac en bar de pescadores.*

Stop off with Rick, living now in Gràcia. Eat at Santa Maria, Cal Pep, Pinotxos. Hallowed places. Frank shares my enthusiasm for shitty bars, for unbelievable food in unlikely places, for the life, the city. Dazzled, we walk and walk. Bring home almonds, saffron, *anxoas*, *Manchego*, *maiz frito*.

Madrid y Sevilla, *enero* 2007

Stay with Frank in Dot's for a night. She works in Madrid now. It's bright, warm, clear, sometimes cold. The sprawling city's wide boulevards, handsome clean-cut men in navy blue suits, women glamorous like you've never seen, the mahogany shine and polished tiles of wine and seafood bars.

Bus south to Seville: olive trees, sugar-coated almonds, *pan de higos*, orange citadels and whitewashed villas, *toreros* dancing in the fields. Balmy Alameda evenings, the remains of Expo '92, the bullring, orange-lined curved streets, the city's punk edge, the procession of the Kings, sweet wrappers, the river— Guadalquivir. Remember flamenco bars, singers in robes, dancers in shadows, ancient voices, movements, echoing down cobbled streets. Read half of *Don Quixote*. Breadsticks!

Barcelona: *algunas veces* 2007–2008

Wealthier, more touristy, slicker, cleaner, trendier (trendy doesn't suit it), but, once attuned, the other Barcelonas are still there to be found. Snappy old *Señores* napping on shaded park benches, proud *abuelas* walking with granddaughters, the moneyed class queuing in capes for the opera. Around the corner in a dimlit bar, a toothless man feeding coins to a machine, an old man drinking cold red wine, smoking, looking at *tetas* in a magazine. *Cafe solo*: *setenta céntimos*. *Entrepan de jamon*: €2.20. *Sisplau*. Absorb the salt, the grime, the constant rumble of traffic, the knife-sharpener's birdsong, the gas-bottle man's barrel clink, the beach-yodel of the coconut vendor.

Barcelona: *más veces* 2008-2010

Frank and I open a bar in Cork, kind of Irish, serving food, kind of Spanish. Quick trip to BCN. Meet Paco, owner and chef of Santa Maria, in his swanky new restaurant. Begin a series of exchanges; he comes to Cork, we cook in BCN. They are great events, memorable. Paco becomes a friend. Barcelona becomes a familiar place. Get to know people who live there, work there.

People in the city begin to recognise us. Learn about new parts of the city, know where to go for *gambas*, for rabbit with *alioli*, to eat *butifarra* and white beans, chickpeas with *morcilla*, good *bravas*, *croquetas caseras*, *cuarto de pollo con papas*, the *menú del dia* with the best *flan de huevo*. Drinking *chupitos* daylong day with Paco, watching the *ping-pongistas* in the park, burning long yellow sticks and rolling balls of soft brown hash into *porros*. Remember the time Antonella came with me to one of the events: me, struck down by food or alcohol or exhaustion in the hotel on Rue Picasso; she, none too impressed.

Barcelona: *septiembre* **2010 –** *noviembre* **2011**

Our business has gone to *mierda*. Frank and I flee to BCN. Paco had said come to Spain, we'll do something. We work and stay with him for a while, but he has his own problems—his father has died, his mother and her boyfriend have lost his money.

Move to Gràcia. Cranes now surround scaffolded Sagrada Familia, as though poised to attack. Heady times. Strained, lonely times. Heartbroken. Frustrated. In debt. But excited. Need a job. Pastry chef. Hard work. Great colleagues. Sixty or so hours a week. Monthly salary: €1,050. Rent and bills: €500. Restaurant life, besides debauched nightlife, becomes my life. Remember watching Barca in local bars with Frank, *vermut* on Sundays, cycling the bustling city day and night, a *pico* cocktail bar's medieval-looking hunchback doorman, weaving up hills past Camp Nou to play football, hanging desperately on to the *moto* in the flashing concrete, neon and steel. Remember coming home at dawn on the subway, or waking up in another part of the city, or the Festa de Gràcia in full swing, mechanical dragons breathing petrol fire, an old man dressed like Barbie on rollerskates. A week dedicated to pleasure. Remember having enough of it all. Too old. Too many suppressed responsibilities. Remember moving home?

Málaga: *septiembre* **2015**

Sully and Maedhbh get married in hills outside Málaga. ¡*Que bonita*! Two nights in Málaga by myself, reconnecting with the world of Spain, letting worries wear away. I speak Spanish. It feels good. To leave Ireland. To be in Spain. To be all together for our friends' marriage. Frank is best man. We're still friends, if a little distant. We opened a BCN-influenced sandwich bar together in Galway, he has since moved back to Cork.

I get drunk every night in Málaga, come home, straight to work, a wreck.

Andalucia: *octubre* 2017

Get some time off. Sarah has different holidays, so I kiss her and depart. Again that wave of relief, of warm, tobacco-tinged air as I leave Málaga airport. Seafront-fried sardines, *castañas* roasting, coffee—sugared and iced. Anchovies. *Jamón y queso*. Breadsticks! To Tarifa. To Cadiz. To temperate, tall-ceilinged bodegas, to deserted beaches, the incessant Levante, Africa hazy in the distance. To *cerveza sin alcohol*, to windmills and reading half of *Don Quixote* again. To Paco, running his own little bar in Rota, a small town with an enormous US military base. Stay a night with him in his farmhouse with the donkey, the horse, and the dog. To *setas. Calabazas. Tostada con chocalate, aceite y sal*. Paco plans on buying a chariot.

Barcelona: *octubre* 2018

Me and Frank go to see a gig. Beach House. Razzmatazz. Don't see enough of Frank these days. We're less a part of each other's lives. Haven't been in Barcelona since I moved back to Ireland. Things have changed, between the city and me, between Frank and me.

Steve picks us up. We eat *bombas* with *salsa rosa* in Gràcia. Meet his girlfriend, a *Mosso de Escuadra*, BCN's feared military police, as she leaves to party with a red-faced cokehead. Frank and Steve drink *medianas*. I'm on *sin alcohol*.

Recognise the street names. Retrace our younger steps. Happy to see *camareros*, aged a little, still working in our favourite bars, saddened to discover the places that have gone. Walk and walk through the city. See: a protest, the ever-growing throngs of tourists, the boutique hotel on Plaça del Sol, the people of Barcelona going about their daily business as the city evolves around them.

Hope to never stop coming here with Frank.

Hope to come here with Sarah, to share this place I love with her.

Somos todos juntos, hermanos y hermanas, amantes, hasta la muerte.

Ghost Writer

Welcome to my studio / maybe we'll click

I work with new and unique voices / booked up all morning

The band broke up in the nineties / through with music history

Yesterday magazine catsuit / today go to Waitrose

Mineral water / would prefer it if you smoked outside

This is just to explore ideas / preferably an upbeat summer release

You never know when / you'll write my next Number One

Pretend I'm not here / that booth 5 is your bedroom

Where do you feel most content / who is listening

When you close your eyes onstage / repeat the chorus

Shadow me / the way my backing vocals underlie a track

The first big hit can shadow you / my name in the credits

Or the next fresh person / fades on the whiteboard

Only the moment a new song / says don't hold me

The way you always do / like stepping off a ledge

Finding the current / every time

Feels just like the first time.

Joe Lines

My Education

To *sashay* is to mispronounce
a French word with your legs,
or—with less judgment—
it is to alter the word
and one's gait. The French
word, *chasser*, I remember
locking into my mind's closet
with a tongue twister
in seventh grade. Translation:
A hunter who knows how to hunt
must know how to hunt without his dog.
When you sashay it is less of a hunt
and more of a stylish chase.
The French teacher's name
was Mr Mann. Later
a different Mr Man (who'd lost
the spare *N*) taught us
history and so did his wife,
Mrs Man, or possibly *Ms*.
By then my French class name
had changed from Giselle
to Lisette. I wanted the syllables
to hang on my frame like
clothes I could not afford
and give me a balletic glow.
Understanding very little
I told Ms Man I was not
a feminist, and Mr Man told us
about the Defenestration of Prague.
There is a word for everything
I thought, but I was wrong,
or else am wrong now, I cannot
tell, I've thrown my mind
through a tall Bohemian window,
and now it is time for a war.

Heather Christle

#MULibraryCat

I look for a poem
to praise you,
and find none.

But there's an amnesty
on book fines
in the library tomorrow,
and I can't help but feel
it was your idea.

Jessica Foley

Neighbour

Sarah Edwards

I'd just moved in, and the parking signs made no sense. Well—they made sense. *Parking Permitted from 6PM to 6PM odd days and 6PM to 6PM even days*. But it seemed too strict to be literal. I thought perhaps the sign had many meanings, like one of those pictures where the rabbit is also a vase. I crossed the street, that first afternoon, to where Sam was sitting on his porch, nearly obscured by a flowering yellow vine.

'It's absurd,' I said. To the vines, or to him.

'Yes,' he said, though I hadn't yet mentioned what I was referencing. 'Isn't it?'

His daughter Claire lived two houses down. She made him dinner sometimes, plates of thinly sliced squash and zucchini from her garden, and they'd eat it out front, and the jar of vinaigrette that rested between them was so large it appeared almost menacing. Once, as I sat on my porch petting the cat, Sam called across the street: 'Come have a bite!'

I started to say yes, but then saw that Claire's body had frozen into a knotty wince and so I just smiled, instead, and shook my head. At the time, having just moved to the area for a PhD programme, I suppose that I also assumed I'd meet somebody my own age to sleep with. Before moving, I'd mapped it all out: the maple trees and long hills cutting up to campus, the book clubs, the flute glasses clinking, the faculty brimming with nineteen-sixties eyewear. It did not happen. Though nearly all the other graduate students in my programme were men and nice enough, they were all unimaginative and anxiously linked to girlfriends with whom they shared vague engagement plans. But the communal coffee pot in the office was always full, never empty, and always emitted a rubbery academic perfume. We worked well together. Everyone shared stories about students and teaching; the weather, too, and little campus politics, which we all seemed to agree on. I excelled in my programme, did better than any of them—my research cleaner, my teaching more developed—but sometimes I became too relaxed. Sometimes I made certain jokes and they'd start to act skittery, foal-like, as if I was plotting to steal them away. Three of the girlfriends that I'd met—all in a row, at someone's thirty-fourth birthday party—had botanical names: 'Ivy' and 'Lily' and 'Danny.'

'Danny?' I'd asked that night, lurching forward on the porch swing. I had not imagined that academic parties would be quite like this: built-up, talked-up, and just as quickly dispersed. Some couple, always, would bring a tiny, fussy cocktail that was impossible to dispense between many people, which then created a feeling, even among the people who had gotten to taste the cocktail, of having been shortchanged.

'Yeah, well,' Danny laughed, 'Short for Dahlia. My parents are big hippies.' The laugh was generous, possibly an invitation. Maybe I wasn't generous, though. Somewhere along the way I'd underestimated the isolating power of second-guessing choices (mine, but also everyone else's). Bad thoughts sprung up, numinous and warped, like mushrooms after rain. When I got home that night I wrote a long, swirling journal entry. I'd had seven beers.

Once, while waiting in line at a coffee shop, I flirted with a law student I often noticed around campus. He was cute and worried-looking. He wore a preppy green jacket which made him look like one of the Beach Boys. I said something daring and probably overly familiar to him while we were waiting for our coffees and he said, 'What?'

That was all he said: 'What?'

It grew cold, exactly as early as everyone had told me it would. The smell of the cold came first, right after the state fair, and then, weeks later—or so it seemed—the sky was thick with snow. Sam came out of his house when I was scraping my windshield off, one morning. I was using a flabby yellow spatula, and he approached, stumbling through snow: 'Hell no, Annie. You're not in the minor leagues anymore.'

The next morning I found an ice scraper, big as a piece of furniture, stuck in my mailbox.

It is likely that Claire knew everything from the beginning. She had two kids and generally seemed to radiate a primal intuition. Still, knowing she might be watching, it took months for me to walk in Sam's front door. I'd thought that I was protecting her by sneaking in, but Sam told me that it just made things worse. His wife—Claire's mother—had died from cancer about a decade before. After she'd died he'd moved out of the country and closer to the university, where he taught engineering courses. He dressed like someone who taught engineering courses, too—nice camping socks, flannel shirts, pants with clips—like a boy scout, vaguely Calvinist, ready for disaster.

Claire often gardened angrily out front wearing a puffy red vest and red knit cap and I admired the metaphor, the performance of wrath. Her emotions seemed raw, practical. She wore T-shirts with the sleeves cut off—not band T-shirts, even, but T-shirts from 5Ks and school fundraisers that made her seem like a seething, suburban version of punk that was far more awe-inspiring than the alternative. She seemed quietly capable of keying my car, of poisoning me. I imagined coming out to my green Honda, one morning, with a dagger drawn down the side of the car, or something more crass. I would've looked up and met her eyes: 'I'm on your side, not mine.'

I knew Claire was three years older than me because Sam had said she was born the year that the Grateful Dead toured Egypt. The math was hazy, but this put Sam somewhere north of sixty. Bearing these facts in mind, I would have hated me, too.

We drove to Sam's cabin one weekend.

'It feels good to be out of the city,' I said gamely and a bit too loudly, and he reached over the gears and squeezed my hand. He recognised nervous language I think, but never seemed to feel a need to spell it out. On the drive up we stopped at several roadside stands, buying an apple—one, two, four—so that by the time we arrived our stomachs were tied in happy, sour knots.

That trip he began to speak more about his wife. On the deck at night, gripping a beer, he described the kind of cancer she'd had—how, after she'd fall asleep, he'd find himself in the dark of his home office without even knowing how he got there, hunched over twisting subterranean internet threads, reading about mainstream cures and alternative cures and alternatives to the alternative cures: legumes, probiotics, prayer, Switzerland, the venom of a scorpion.

'I became a cancer henchman,' he said. 'Like an obsessive henchman, but for good.'

The pines moved slightly, nodding.

The cancer was a specific kind I happened to know a lot about but I didn't say so. I just stood there beside him, leaning against the deck railing, listening as the wind and the trees moved, greasing the dark. At one point I shivered and he directed me inside to a drawer of her old Vassar sweatshirts. I stood there for a long time, deciding, and then pulled one on that hadn't yet faded to pink.

At the beginning of the next school year I saw the solar eclipse. With undergraduates and townies, I stood beneath a grove of swaying trees for forty-five minutes, waiting to look through a small brown telescope. Standing in that bright, rippling bay of shadow cutlets, I'd felt a bit of vertigo: the world turned lunar and sidewise. A line I'd heard in Sunday School came back and moved through me: 'You have a God-shaped hole in you.' Oh, I thought. I wondered for a few days if this new brightness inside me was a cluster of pregnancy hormones. I lay awake at night thinking of it, of them, imagining them as they must have looked. Like a city, lit from above.

My period had arrived on the first of the month, like it always did, but I'd long felt that I'd be one of those people whose body defied the medical establishment, who took too many vitamins and died, or who went into a coma and woke up speaking another language. Epiphanies about my life, my desires, bloomed hot and lucid; a rapid flower within me.

I spent a week working up the courage and then bought three tests at the pharmacy, lying to the pierced boy at the checkout: 'My niece—she's extremely irresponsible.' But they weren't pregnancy hormones. The tests were definitive. Biology worked. Did that realisation make me happy or sad? It seemed impossible to say. It seemed I had watched too many cleaning commercials, the mop cutting a shining, psychedelic diagonal across the kitchen floor, to ever fully know which of these thoughts were mine and which belonged to advertising.

I'd had ongoing problems with my landlord, who looked like Billy Joel and was very corrupt, and so I broke my lease. It seemed like a good idea to move, to shift things. I also broke up with Sam. When I told him (gently, I thought), he got up from the couch and walked around the house opening and shutting drawers, as if he were looking for something. I actually thought, maybe he has something to give me? Maybe I will change my mind? But he came back after a while and touched my knee.

'You're right. It's probably the right thing.'

When I went to leave he stood by the door. 'Can we still talk?'

Of course, I said. We'll talk.

We bore through one phone conversation and then ran into each other a few times—in the student union, crossing the street, at a university function, where we stood on a hard grey carpet and wagged paper champagne cups around in terrible circles. After that, it seemed best to avoid West Campus altogether.

I struck up a friendly thing with the law student I'd admired from afar, who actually did wear sixties glasses, or something like them. And that green jacket! It thrilled me all through summer and into the fall. First, we studied near each other—across the room, across the table, and then two seats apart, idling like cars. Eventually, we both stood up, walked down the long hallway, stepped outside, and pulled out our respective packs of cigarettes.

'I am obsessed with Mumblecore,' he said another time, while we were standing outside the library awning. He had an expansive mouth and he opened it wide, letting out an athletic crack. It sounded like a champagne bottle uncorking.

'Greta Gerwig,' I nodded, agreeing. I fished out another cigarette.

A few months later, taking another smoke break, he became confessional. 'Sometimes I am actually afraid that I might be in a Mumblecore film.'

'Like *The Truman Show*?' I said, though I hadn't meant it as a question.

'Oh, no.' He looked staggered. 'Not like *The Truman Show* at all.'

When we finally slept together it was four in the afternoon, after we'd spent nearly an hour passing a shared cider back and forth in his kitchen and talking a bit about a minor university scandal. Nothing that either of us really cared about, the kind of thing so contentious it had become neutral. After a while, we fell quiet. He'd nod, and then I'd nod, and then I'd stick my mouth over the cider as if to blow a musical note. I felt desire but it was the sloping, contractual kind associated with trying to get out of a rut. When he excused himself to go to the bathroom I opened one of his kitchen cabinets. There were two pale yellow bowls and a giant blender sitting in it. Cobwebs spackling the sideboard, nothing more. I shut the cabinet quickly and went to look out at the backyard. Already, the world outside was scattered with pinholes of living-room light. It had started getting dark early again; grey gone dark grey, the kind of daytime/nighttime tangle that confuses people, like staring into a mirror too long. I stood there and tried to remember if I had ever slept with somebody for the first time stone-cold sober and in the middle of the day. It seemed unlikely.

It was nothing like the hot corkscrew splash that came when you were alone. I'd forgotten that. Though with Sam, there had at least been the talking. He liked to describe my shape. I don't mean in a politically incorrect way. I just mean a sort of dreamy, drifting sort of chatter while we lay in bed. Most of the time he'd been quiet, bordering on too quiet; full of long pauses and easy smiles. Lying in bed, though, something seemed to unlatch. He seemed to never tire of praising. He liked my legs and the way the backs of my elbows folded up into a U-turn. He liked the way my hair smelled. We joked about a certain drugstore shampoo I used, which claimed to smell like ISLAND (although which island, the shampoo never specified). This cracked him up, got him good. 'Ahhhh, the ambiguous scent of island,' he would say while stroking my hair, singling out the new greys with his fingers.

He liked other things about me, too—the swingy way I walked, my collection of jelly jars, my smudged brown clogs, my work ethic. My clavicles. I liked his hands. I liked that he didn't construct his jokes like he was asking for a favour. I *loved* the 'ambiguous island' joke. I liked that he was good to his daughter, that he was good to me.

I could tell that the law student also admired my body—I'd taken up swimming laps over the summer and my legs were now stronger, more sculpted, like Diane Lane's—but he didn't speak until we were finished.

'Christ,' he said, sitting up and shifting, hanging his head between his legs. He shuddered again. There was a salty ribbon running down his back. 'God.'

Without his glasses, he looked blanched and bewildered. He fished a silky pair of basketball shorts out from beneath his pillow and pulled them on.

Then he said, 'I can walk you home.'

'Matthew,' I said. 'I biked here.'

He knew I had. He owned a bike pump and my tires needed air; that had been the whole pretext, or pretence, of our afternoon.

'I still feel like I should walk you home,' he said with a kind of courtly deference. And then added, humbly, 'I'm out of food, anyways. I need takeout.'

On the walk back we talked about California, where he was from, and briefly the conversation hummed. He told me that his sister, who he spoke to almost every day, was a semi-professional teenage surfer. She was training for something called the Billabong Pipe Masters and had been to prom fourteen times.

'My God,' I said, blankly.

Humour hopped up around his eyes unexpectedly, like a little Chickadee. 'Not me, though,' he said. 'I watched *Donnie Darko* the night of my prom.'

I returned the smile. I wondered, for a moment, if maybe there had been a sweetness underlying the whole afternoon that I had somehow missed. As we continued walking, a breeze sent a rusty tremor through the leaves and improbably, one of the frat houses on the main drive began blasting Morrissey.

At the crosswalk, a flash of gold dropped to the ground. I was steering my bike, and felt a current of panic; a strong, sick need to keep walking. I felt that if I stopped and looked back, I might experience a tremendous unspooling. Lot's wife—the earring dissolved, the city dissolved, and me in it. The world salty and crystallised. Everything I loved reduced to mineral.

The law student had noticed. 'I think something dropped.'

'What?'

'Something dropped,' he repeated, and then looked at my ear. 'One of your earrings.'

'It's fine.' The walk signal turned red. The earring was half of my favourite pair—bright, twisted droplets that my best friend Rebecca had bought at an art fair, a few years before she died.

'Your earring dropped,' he repeated again, though he didn't offer to retrieve it. 'Don't you want it?'

I thought of those two pale yellow bowls stacked in the pantry, the ashy bug detritus pooled in the bottom—he was young, in the way grown men are allowed to be. He was lucky. He had another ten, maybe fifteen, years in his late-twenties. But he meant no harm.

Nothing had felt urgent for weeks, but now I felt a sense of urgency so strong, so brave and thin and flapping, that I wanted to cry.

'I have a meeting with my advisor,' I said, 'I forgot that I had one, but I just remembered that I have one.'

'Now? It's, like, 8PM.'

'You're telling me.'

He shook his head sadly. 'God, well. Okay.'

'So dumb,' I mounted my bike. 'Old men who think I don't have a life.'

I was completely sober. Oh, the big, big moon! The ragged trees! I breezed past the brewery and Korean restaurant and vape shop until, suddenly, I was on my old block. The streetlights were different than in my memory—milkier, warm and blushing. The lawn chairs were covered in pine needles and I was alarmed to see that cars were parked on both sides of the street. This bothered me. Wouldn't they get tickets? Shouldn't somebody let them know? The old neighbour's grey cat came padding across the cul-de-sac, circling my ankles. I felt flattered that she remembered; she'd always passed over me, stalking through the neighbourhood like an angel of death. I knelt and held out my hand to her, but she backed away, hissing as if affronted.

I looked across the street. The lights in his house were off.

The key was still under the Begonia pot but I went to the backyard anyways and crawled onto the air conditioning unit, pushing aside branches. They were thicker, more portentous, than I remembered. It took some tugging but the window finally jerked stiffly up—this part was just as I recalled—and my foot found the sofa inside.

A brief thrill, as I surveyed the living room again as a forbidden lover, a Romeo of Onondaga County. I walked through the room touching objects as if I had never seen them before; not looking at them, only touching and feeling. Standing in the dark of the kitchen I reached into the fridge and took a long, reckless swig of orange juice. It tasted like vinegar.

His wife had kept bees. I knew this because the website advertising her honey still existed, if you looked hard enough. It was the kind of relic, like a Myspace page, that most people would want scrubbed: homemade, pastel and peach-toned, written in a bulky, vulnerable font. It was of a different time. It was of a time before you knew that a website design could be embarrassing, even if you were selling things—pure, antibacterial things—like honey and soap. But somehow the page had survived, still advertising buckwheat honey varieties in three- and five-pound jars. The 'About Me' page showed her smiling in a giant white beekeeping suit, looking like she'd just made it to the moon. At least, I got the impression that she was smiling; the suit was obscuring. But really it seemed that there was a person inside it who was smiling, who was all lit-up. That the blimp of a suit was lit from the inside.

I found Sam in his bed, the quilt flung messily over his body. He didn't move when I came in. I paused at the door, filled with a lonely thrill at standing in the room again. It had been almost a year since I'd last seen him like this. He always had several loafers kicked under the window and tonight the moon was shining directly onto them, contouring them into a pile of diamonds.

'Sam,' I said. But he had always been a hard sleeper. 'SAM. Let's go to the cabin. Let's go this weekend.'

I waited a moment and then started over again, moving closer. I said that I felt—that I knew—that we were finally over the hard part. I would try with Claire, and he'd see that, and she'd see that, and the world was full of strange, unlikely families and truly, truly, some holy flashlight had beamed across my awful heart and filled me with light. Finally, I saw this. We could be one of those happy families.

I traced the elastic of his boxers and drew it playfully back to snap, but the fabric fell loosely and still, he didn't stir. Tenderness roared through me: I saw that it was my job to buy him a pack of new boxers, that it was my job to protect him. I crawled onto the bed and lay there for a while and the scent that eventually settled across the room was quite nearly overwhelming; a cold new musk, like almond and hay.

Quickly, While They Still Have Horses

Jan Carson

Paola would not come home to meet his parents.

'I am not good with mothers,' she said, and left the table suddenly so the conversation couldn't go any further.

Paola would not come home for Christmas.

'I don't like Christmas,' she said. 'It gives me sadness behind my eyes.' She pointed out the exact spots where the sadness would swell to form bad memories and migraine headaches. 'Here, and here.'

He went home without Paola, leaving her to Christmas alone in their Camden flat, which was above a launderette and smelt like summer should smell, even in December. Before leaving he bought perfume and tucked it inside the fridge door, so she'd find it and know he hadn't abandoned her entirely. It was expensive perfume, the sort displayed behind the counter in Boots, the name of it written in sloped French. When he returned, just in time for New Year, the perfume was still in the fridge, still giftwrapped and wedged between the margarine and a jar of own-brand marmalade.

'I suppose I didn't see it,' Paola said. 'There are so many other things to see when I'm in the fridge: for example, cheese and tomatoes and the light which is always turning on when the door opens.'

He didn't entirely believe her. Nor did he doubt her ability to see only those things she wished to see. She opened the perfume to please him and wore it out on New Year's Eve. The smell of it was not strong enough to overpower the soap soft smell of laundered air. He wished he'd spent his money on good wine instead.

Paola would not come home for his sister's wedding, or his other sister's baby, or the possibility of seeing, firsthand, all his growing-up places. Vicky Park, where he'd learned to ride a bike, weaving his way through the swans and vicious greylag geese. The sweetie shop in Ballyhack. The bus shelter at the Holywood Arches where he'd had his first dry kiss and the alley opposite where, later that night, the same girl had let him slip the tongue in. Paola was not tempted by the scenery, even when he showed her pictures on the internet. Together, they watched television programmes which had been filmed at home on account of the tax breaks and the lovely scenery. 'Look at it,' he said, 'isn't it gorgeous?'

Paola looked hard at the hills and the windswept beaches. Eventually, she said, 'It's ok, I guess. There are better beaches in Spain. It's not raining on those beaches.'

Paola would not come home for a dirty weekend at the Port, or half-term in the mountains, or even the Twelfth, which he tried to sell as a genuine cultural experience. He knew this was something of a long shot, but could no longer anticipate what weird shit would catch her interest. The previous week she'd expressed a desire to learn quilting. This week it'd been calligraphy. He had never seen Paola as the sort of person who'd practise craft of any kind. She was never still. She was something like a hovercraft, buzzing with nervous energy.

No matter what he said or implied—love, duty, some kind of unspoken, 'I'll owe you big time'—Paola would not come home with him.

This didn't seem fair. They'd been together for almost two years, two and a half if you counted the months of trying to talk themselves out of each other. Granted, he hadn't been to Spain, or met any of her family, but she'd never asked. She found her parents deplorable, and Spain was much further away. In his outside head he told himself, *Never mind, you only want her home so everyone can see you have an exotic, continental girlfriend now; so, all the lads will be jealous, embarrassed by their own doughy women.* In his inside head, he knew he was softer than this. He understood, without admitting, the desire to have everything he loved together in one easy place.

'Would you not come home for *me*, Paola?' he kept on asking. 'Just because you love me.' But she always said, 'No. No. No chance, Buster,' each individual *no* wrapped up in its own neat excuse like a filling buried so deep inside a back tooth you couldn't see the problem with it.

Paola would not come home for anything he said or did until, one day, he heard from his mother, on the telephone, that they still had horses in Belfast.

'They've two or three of them left,' she said. 'There's one in Ormeau Park and another in Botanic. You can get tickets from City Hall. It's free but you've to wait your turn. Your Auntie Liz says the line's all the way down to Primark now.'

When he told Paola about the horses she wanted to leave immediately.

'We must go to your home,' she said, 'quickly, while they still have horses.'

'I never knew you were into horses,' he said, all the time wondering what else he didn't know about her: birthmarks, allergies, previous marriages to much older men.

'Oh, I'm not that specially interested in horses,' she said. 'They're ok, I guess. I am much more into fish. But I don't like the idea that they're here and then, the next day, gone—poof—like David Bowie or that other singer who is also dead. I don't have a just-for-myself memory of Bowie. It was too expensive to see him live in concert. Now I can't. I do not want to have such regrets with horses. Horses will not be like David Bowie to me. We must take a picture of us standing with this last horse, smiling. Later, we will show the photograph to our grandchildren and say, 'Look at us, so young in this picture. They actually still had horses then.'

He thought Paola was a little mad, or perhaps just continental, but the idea that they might last long enough to produce grandchildren was reassuring. He wondered if they would one day own a house together or, if a house was out of the question, a small apartment or mobile home like the one his grandparents kept at Portrush.

He put the flights on his credit card and texted his mother: 'Me and Paola are coming home. Can we stay with you?'

His mother texted straight back. (She always did. Even during church). 'That will be lovely. Is Paula a vegetarian?'

Paola was not a vegetarian, but his mother assumed all continentals were anti-meat. 'I could do a nice salad for lunch,' she added in a second text, 'with olives.' He didn't bother replying. He knew it was going to be a long weekend.

Paola didn't sleep that night. She sat up in their bed googling images of horses on his work laptop.

'Look at this one, running,' she said, 'Look at this one, up on its back legs like a statue of itself.'

He'd always been a feeble sleeper, so instead of trying to sleep through her talk, he sat up beside her, faking an interest in shire horses, piebald ponies and previous Grand National winners, all the time thinking, *Tomorrow she is coming home with me.* There was a tune that accompanied this thought. It was something like the chorus of a good Smiths song, which is to say it was hooked and chirpy, a little like a playground taunt. *Tomorrow, tomorrow, Paola is coming home with me.*

Finally, Paola closed the laptop and set it aside. He thought she might be ready to sleep then, or that she'd want to have sex (as she often did on a Thursday). He touched her lightly on the spot where her neck became a shoulder. This was his usual way of asking. She didn't say no. Instead she turned her back to him and asked, 'Do *you* like horses?'

He did *not* like horses.

Once, as a child, his grandfather had given him polo mints with which to feed the horse who spent most days shuffling round the field next to his grandparents' bungalow. Polo mints, his grandfather said, were treats for horses, like ice cream was for children, while hay was just like everyday vegetables.

His grandfather hadn't shown him how to hold the polo mint, like a little bird balanced in the flat of his palm, so he'd pinched the sweet between finger and thumb, stretching his arm over the fence to let the horse get a good, long whiff of it. Suddenly, before he could withdraw, the horse's teeth had clamped around his fingers. His face became damp with hot horse breath. All the blood ran to his fingers and he began to shriek. Panic set in. He couldn't get away. The pain was dull and prolonged, like a heavy weight pressing into a bruise.

'OH SHITE!' his grandfather had shouted, the first time he'd ever heard a bad word on the old man's tongue. He'd pulled hard at his grandson's trapped arm, tugging and sharply tugging, digging his boot heels into the sloped verge that ran beneath the fence, grunting with effort as his feet slipped around on the damp grass until finally the horse opened its mouth and let go. They hadn't toppled backwards, like in a film, and there was no blood, but he'd known straightaway that the finger would bruise. Later when he thought about this incident, he'd picture his grandfather pulling him by the waist, bracing his feet against the ground and leaning away from the weight of him, like the old man in his fairytale book, with his wife dragging at his waist, the neighbours and farmyard animals all strung out behind.

The horse left teethmarks in his fingers. He could still see the pale pink ghost of them when he was hot and sweating from sport, or outside in the sun. Paola had never noticed. She didn't pay particular attention to his fingers. He could have held them under her nose and said, 'Look at this here mark,' and told her the story of the Polo-mint horse. But he didn't. He couldn't risk anything that might put her off coming home.

'I love horses,' he lied. 'If I get the chance, I'd really like a wee ride on that last one. So, I can tell the grandchildren.'

He wanted to see if the mention of grandchildren would make Paola smile, but when he leant over her shoulder to look, her mouth had slipped into the loose shape it always made when sleeping. It was no closer to a smile than a frown.

The next morning, they flew home. Paolo was insistent that they go straight to the horses, so they took a taxi from the airport to City Hall.

Paola did not like Belfast. First, it was too rainy. Then, it was not as rainy as she'd expected. The people were watery looking, or maybe they looked like potatoes round the face, all pasty skinned and lumpy. 'I do not find anyone attractive here,' she said, 'not even the young girls.' He wondered if she included him in this judgement but hadn't the gall to ask.

'And the houses,' she said, 'don't get me started on the houses,' and rolled her eyes towards the taxi's roof. She said the houses were all stuck together like they couldn't breathe. Those that weren't were mostly bungalows and Paola had no time for single-storey buildings. She said the hills were ugly, hardly worth a photograph. She wondered what they'd done with the coastline, why they'd hidden it behind all those shipping cranes as if beaches weren't the very best way to frame an ocean. She said the accent was 'freeking impossible', that the people talked much too fast, through their noses. Whiney. Whine. Whine. Like stretched rubber.

'Sure, you must be used to it by now,' he said. 'Haven't I the very same accent?'

'Exactly,' she said, and all afternoon he was overly conscious of the way his mouth moved when he spoke.

When they arrived at City Hall, they dragged their pull-on suitcases up the cobbled path, round the statue of Queen Victoria looking like she'd absolutely no interest in the city, and past the impressively pillared entrance. Chu-choonk. Chu-choonk. Chu-choonk went the suitcase wheels. The line was out the door and round the War Memorial twice. Most people looked defeated, like they'd been standing in line for years, neither experiencing nor expecting any significant progress. Everyone turned to stare at them. It was raining, absolutely pissing down, and they hadn't brought an umbrella.

'We'll be here all afternoon,' he said.

'I don't do lines,' Paola replied.

Before he could stop her she was striding up the steps and through the marbled foyer to the front of the queue. She was telling the desk lady that he was dying of 'the Cancer'—'belly cancer', to be specific—and wasn't able to stand on his own two feet for hours in the rain. Quite conveniently, the desk lady had a neighbour, recently dead, of 'belly cancer'. She understood it was the sorest cancer of them all. Back Paola came with a wheelchair and a big, black umbrella to keep the rain off his poorly head.

'Look sick,' she said. 'Hold your belly like it is full of painful tumours.'

'What did you tell them?' he asked.

'Only, that you're dying. That you want to see a horse before it's too late.'

'Jesus,' he said, 'you can't be making up stuff like that. There's probably folks in this queue actually dying.' But he got into the wheelchair anyway, letting her manhandle him past the line, over the juddery cobbles, and up the ramp into City Hall.

Paola parked him in the corner of the foyer by the stained-glass window commemorating Votes for Women. She arranged their luggage in a little tower beside his wheelchair, so he felt like a pilgrim waiting on the bus to Lourdes. He felt, as always, less than her, and dependent.

'Don't move,' she said. Her tone was matronly but her body language was far from it. She leant heavily on his lap, kissing him softly on the cheek. Up close, he could smell the fancy perfume on her.

'I love you,' he said.

She smiled. The light streaming through the stained-glass window was red, blue and cut grass green, and fell across her face, marbling her olive skin. He thought, as he often thought, *There's something not quite right about this woman*. This was half the pull of her.

Leaving him with their luggage, Paola approached the counter and asked to speak to the nice desk lady in the white blouse. He could hear the sound of her, over-annunciating, all the way across the rotunda. She was using the voice she kept for small children.

'We need two tickets to the horse,' she said.

'We'll get you sorted out, pet,' said the desk lady. She printed out two tickets and slid them across the counter. Paola was always encountering this kind of preferential treatment.

'Why do you still have horses here?' Paola asked and he wondered why she'd not asked him; what other questions she'd taken to strangers.

The lady paused and glanced up at Paola. She smiled. He recognised this smile. It was a smile the people here kept for visitors. He'd often used it himself on American relations. If this smile was a sentence it would have read, 'Ah now, it's a local thing. How would you be expected to know when you're not from round here?'

'We're losing our horses too, sweetheart,' said the desk lady. 'They're just a drain on the economy, so say the politicians anyway. The horses on the mainland are all gone now, either culled or shipped to places where they still use horses for pulling carts, or where they'll eat anything. It's a shame, so it is. Horses are lovely creatures to look at even if they are no use. If you ask me, they'll be after cats next. It's not like there's any point in a cat.'

'I know all that,' Paola said, interrupting the desk lady mid flow, 'I watch the news. I was just asking why you still have horses here when the rest of Britain has already lost theirs.'

The lady smiled the same slow smile. 'Well, the mainland's already adopted the new legislation. You can't keep a horse over there because horses don't do anything of any real use… And we get everything six months after the mainland.' Then, she lent away from the counter, as if she'd just delivered the punchline to a great old joke. Across the foyer, he also smiled. He couldn't help himself.

When Paola returned, she was not smiling. She looked tired. 'I do not like this place,' she said. He knew she was actually trying to say, 'I do not understand this place.' This place that was all the way through him like blood, like bone. Still, he wished to sit her down on a chair and say, 'Hold it all loosely, girl. Give it time. Try to see the funny side. There's good stuff here too. You've just to wait on it.'

'Let's go to the horse,' she said, 'before I change my mind.'

'Where is the horse?' he asked.

'Botanic Gardens,' she replied. 'There is no room for horses at City Hall.'

Paola did not question the sense of selling tickets to an attraction almost fifteen minutes away though she did seem somewhat weary. Perhaps she was beginning to understand the perverse logic of this place.

She wheeled him out to the gates of City Hall, where he made a seemingly miraculous recovery, rising from his wheelchair to hail a black taxi. He bundled her into the backseat. Up the Dublin Road they flew, past the cinema and all the student bars, past Queen's University and the stout gates of Methodist College, to Botanic Gardens, where there was a horse waiting for them.

'It's the last one, mate,' said the taxi driver, 'the very last horse in Britain.'

'But there's one in Ormeau Park?' he said. 'And another one somewhere round Monaghan?'

'Them one's died,' said the taxi driver, 'Loneliness, I'd say. Horses are wild social. Same goes for penguins.' Here, his wisdom ran dry.

Paola tipped the taxi man two pounds because she liked penguins. He tried to tell her you didn't do that here, that the driver would think them flash or, worse still, tourists, and Paola said, 'But we are tourists,' and he wondered if this was true. It was five years since he'd lived here for more than a fortnight, and just thinking about this made him feel like he was wearing a jumper one size too small.

Botanic Gardens was hiving with people. The rain had morphed into a sad drizzle. The people lined along the path waited listlessly in damp, waterproof jackets, their bowed heads hooded and glistening so they looked like uprooted plants waiting to be rehomed. There was a special enclosure for the horse in the middle of the Gardens. A sign read, 'LAST HORSE IN BRITAIN this way', with an arrow so you couldn't mistake it for the Tropical Ravine. The gardeners had constructed a sort of paddock, running a ten-foot fence round the green so you couldn't see anything worth seeing without paying for the privilege. There was another line, and they took their place at the end of it.

It was mostly children in front of them and adults who might've been using their children as an excuse. Paola tried to skip the queue using the cancer card again, but the man two in front said, 'Sorry for your trouble, girl, but I've a wife with Alzheimer's here, and I'm not giving up our spot.'

So they waited for an hour and a half edging their pull-on luggage forward one foot at a time. They ate dry roasted peanuts from Paola's handbag to stave off the hunger and, for shelter, ducked their damp heads under the canopy of tree branches tickling the edges of the green. By three they were inside the paddock, by three thirty surrendering their tickets to a young lad in a luminous vest.

'No flash photography,' he said. 'No videos. Will you be wanting a ride on the horse or do youse just want to get your picture with it?'

'A ride would be great,' he said. The teethmarks on his finger began to sing in anticipation.

'I am fine with just the photograph,' said Paola. 'Both of us together with the horse.'

He could not have been easier in his own skin, or happier, with a money fortune. Up came the jangly Smithsonian refrain, '*Paola's coming home with me…* ' Up came the memory of horses and her and growing up in this fine place. It was all muddled together like a Saturday evening stew. Grandparents were in there and hometown God, his parents and the lads he used to kick football with, big school, wee school, sheet rain and street preachers howling, Portstewart Strand for the holidays, the gut twist relief of belonging somewhere specific. He was glad that Paola was here with him, seeing the horse. She would understand now, what it meant to be from this place.

'In you go, mate,' said the young lad, opening the Tensabarrier and ushering them into the inner enclosure. 'There's the wee horse there. He goes by Buttons. Youse are welcome to take as many photos as you want.'

Buttons was not a horse so much as a pony. A dog-sized pony. He looked up at them from under an enormous fringe, his eyes sunken raisins, blinking back the flies. He was the colour of damp sand.

'I thought it would be different,' he said. By different, he meant bigger. He could feel Paola standing behind him, saying nothing, thinking about Spanish horses thundering across Spanish beaches.

'That's the last horse left, mate. They kept Buttons 'til the end cos he's so good with the wee ones. Like a kitten he is, round children and ones with special needs.'

'I understand,' he said, though really, he didn't. 'Sure, we'll just get our picture with him and be off. Paola, give the man your camera.'

'But you said you wanted a ride on the last horse,' she said. 'You said that.'

He looked at Paola. Her hair was plastered across her forehead. Her leopard-print suitcase leant against her ankles. She was less poised than usual but still in control of the situation. He tried to say with his eyes, 'Have some mercy,' or, 'This could be the end of us.' He wanted to ask her, 'Do you not think I've suffered enough?' But he could see she was a brick wall now.

'Get on the horse,' she said, 'and I will take your picture for our grandchildren.'

He did what he was told. He was well-practised at this.

He climbed the fence. He straddled the horse, holding its reins loosely in one hand. There was a good half-foot of air between his crotch and the saddle, but he couldn't risk the humiliation of squatting bow-legged in front of her. So, he stood over the very last horse, smiling a different kind of smile, equally hard learnt.

'Got it,' Paola said, and put her camera back into its holder. He knew she wouldn't agree to a photograph, so he didn't bother asking. He could see she was already looking for the exit. She was halfway back to Camden in her head.

'What about our grandchildren?' he wanted to ask. 'What about our small apartment or mobile home?' He felt small in her eyes now, small and faintly ludicrous. He struggled to imagine them recovering from the horse.

Maybe, he thought, there might still be a chance. Compromises would need to be made, of course, and he knew he'd be the one to make them. He could, with effort, picture the pair of them together at forty, in London, or Spain, or perhaps, the States. But, not here, suffocating, in this damp excuse of a place.

Small Change:
A Sequence on Money, Writing and Value

A few years ago, the writer and illustrator Molly Crabapple wrote that 'not talking about money is a tool of class war.' It's a formulation that struck me immediately as true, and I've thought of it often since. When it's not just awkward, talking about money is traditionally seen as somewhat crass. There are, after all, much finer things in life. On the level of the soul, perhaps, money is not all that important. But the soul lives on the bread of the body, and the body lives on actual bread, and actual bread costs actual money.

Money is not often talked about. The things money can buy so often stand in for money itself. We see an expensive object—a car, a house, a holiday, fine clothes—and we fill in the rest. Money is, for most people, something you receive for spending part of your life engaged in work for someone else—that person buys your time from you with money. And perhaps most people, if they had the money, would simply buy that time back. Once the rent is paid and the groceries are packed away, time is what people so often spend their money on—time in which to be not working; time in which to be working on something which is not 'work' per se; time in which to create the thing that could make you money with which you could buy more time.

Mia Gallagher's essay in this issue, delivered as a lecture at the Bray Literary Festival, is a comprehensive treatment of the relationship between time, money, art, and ego. It's about the way various different conceptions of value—personal, social, literary, financial—commingle in the act, or practice, of writing. I think it's timely and illuminating.

The pieces which follow—by Conor McCabe, Muireann O'Dwyer, Arnold Thomas Fanning and Elske Rahill—are each distinct meditations on similar themes: what does money mean? Which contributions get valued, and which overlooked? Who pays, and how much, and for what? Often this is a concrete concern—we all have to eat—but just as often it's something more abstract, something to do with our sense of ourselves, our self-worth; our courage, our resolve, our jealousy, our happiness.

Money, as Conor McCabe writes, is a human invention. Perhaps we could go further and say it is the *most* human invention—the invention which, for better or worse, is most deeply embedded in our daily lives. It's not everything, and it doesn't make you happy, but, as my grandfather used to say, you won't get far without it. So let's talk about it.

—Ian Maleney

€$£ €$£ €$£

MONEY IS A HUMAN INVENTION. It is not a gift from the gods or a by-product of nature, nor is it found in a hole in the ground. It is a social technology, one of the oldest we have. It was the basis, along with numeracy and writing, for the world's first large-scale complex societies. It owes its existence to people and to the dynamics of social organisation, exchange and circulation. Without these elements, money is nothing.

Money allows for the movement of obligations, possessions, goods, services, promises, debts and legacies between people. It is 'a mode of mobilising resources,' wrote the historian Christine Desan, 'one that communities design for that end and individuals appropriate for their own purposes.' For this to happen, things of value must be expressed in monetary terms and have the ability to be converted into money. This process is not always equal, not always democratic, and if unchecked, social wealth once monetised will congeal around a very small but powerful section of society. The money system contains within it the ability to concentrate social value in the hands of a few, even though such value is created through the actions of many. When we start to look at the money system as a system, it becomes clear that there is more to money than markets.

Money cannot be comprehended in isolation, as a thing in itself. To see the form that money takes—be it notes, coins, or bank account digits—and not the societal dynamics that underpin that form, is to miss entirely the purpose, structure and power of money and the money system. It is dependent on law, as well public and private institutions such as central banks, government departments, commercial banks and financial markets. It cannot transcend its social and legal setting and remain as money. The modern Irish pound was in effect from 1927 to 2002. Its main value today is to collectors on eBay.

Money is not neutral. It has powerful distributional effects. It operates simultaneously through the realms of value, law, and time. It is abstract and powerful, and actively shapes the world it inhabits. We can lend it, work for it, win it, steal it, borrow it or receive it through various supports, but in order to maintain ourselves we need to get our hands on it. This involuntary compulsion to attain money, the coercive power that the money nexus wields, is in sharp contrast to the view that the desire for money is one of greed and little else. We need money to survive, and for most people that is compulsion enough.

In other words, money is social and political. It only comes alive through a dynamic between people, institutions, law, and the state. We see it as a thing (notes and coins) but we experience it as an activity (buying, selling, working, renting, saving, lending, investing, etc.). A man on a desert island who sits on a pile of gold coins is waiting for a ship to arrive so he can put them to use. The coins on the island will not make corn cultivate itself or through their mere presence turn metal into a spear. Money viewed separately from society is the same as viewing words separately from grammar. It is babble, etchings without meaning. We cannot focus solely on the mere 'words' of money (notes, coins, digits) if we want to understand it; we also need to study its 'grammar'—that is, the underlying structure that gives money its expressive and interpretative logic.

Societies change, of course, and the structural dynamic and focus of money changes with them. The world we live in today is a capitalist world. We may still use essentially the same type of money forms as ancient and feudal societies—coins, credit notes, paper currency—but that does not mean we use them in the same way, and for entirely the same purposes. To restate, the logic of money does not come from money itself: it is a societal logic and that changes over time.

Capitalism has its own logic, of course, the essence of which is the hunt for yield (return on investment). That is its core organisational principle. It monetises nature and human activity based on the presumption that such monetisation will produce a profitable return. It transforms societies and devours people and nature to meet this objective.

As citizens we are required to support the profit-seeking strategies of financial institutions that have significant control over money and credit, but we are not supposed to question those strategies, the logic that underpins them, nor the power relations that envelop its world. Money is just a thing, the economists say, one that is too complicated for ordinary and feeble minds.

However, far from being neutral, money is an extremely powerful tool, one that demands our attention. It works through powerful relationships of constructed meanings, including abstract representations of value. These are socially grounded. They are not separable entities that can be changed like the wheels on a car.

This makes alternatives to money—community exchange systems, cryptocurrencies, or local currencies such as the Bristol Pound—a bit of a false trail. The state and institutional dynamic of the capitalist money-system is not challenged by such ventures, which allows them to operate as complementary currencies rather than as actual, societal alternatives. If you want to make a more equitable and democratic money system, you have to tackle the logic of capitalism that has *invaded* the money system—that is, the logic of extractive accumulation for monetised profit—and that takes organisation and a plan. The money system can be democratised to work for society as a whole, but only as part of a wider democratisation of social value for the common good. In order to do this, a commonwealth of progressive forces is needed, one that involves civil society, organised labour, and political representatives working in tandem with agreed principles in terms of work, health, housing, child care, education, taxation, and the environment. The direction that this collective action might pursue is itself something that can only be worked out through praxis—that is, through action and reflection—and because of this its shape and form cannot be predicted with any certainty. It is a project that requires ongoing education, research, organisation, and activism, if it is to have any chance of success. This will not be easy, but it can be done.

—Dr Conor McCabe

€$£ €$£ €$£

I ALWAYS TELL STUDENTS to look out for the silences—by spotting the things that aren't being talked about, we can understand the broader power dynamics of politics. And in the academic world that I work in, there is a strange silence around money. Maybe everyone is talking about things like salary negotiations without me, but I don't think so. This lack of discussion of pay is one of the factors that many studies show lead to things like gender and race pay gaps. In the UK, according the University and College Union, women are paid on average 15 per cent less than men, while black academics earn 12 to 13 per cent less than white colleagues of the same gender and experience.

We also don't talk all that much about the other ways that money shapes our work and our profession. For example, the system of conferences that require payment of a registration fee, travel costs, accommodation costs, and often visa costs as well, is built on assumptions of stable employment and a generous research allowance. Waiting for reimbursements becomes a much more stressful experience if you are already underpaid and facing rising rent or bills. But, despite increased awareness of such problems, the solutions remain limited. There are those with very good intentions, using what little resources they may have to rectify massive, structural problems, and to try to develop funding supports for conferences or workshops, usually aimed at those who are excluded from traditional supports. However, many of these supports have become yet another aspect of how money becomes part of the overall academic fetish for quantifying our success, our impressiveness. Travel grants become yet another accolade that must be displayed on the academic CV, referenced in the job application—'Look, I'm valuable, someone valued me, they spent money on me and my work!'

Any cursory look at the distribution of salaries, not just in academia but really everywhere, will quickly disprove that money and value should be equated. Yet, money still plays an important role in signalling what those who make the money decisions choose to value. Employers and funders are constantly making such value judgements. This ties money up with broader power structures, giving gate-keepers control over livelihoods, as well as the overall debate. This makes certain types of work feel more valuable, simply because they are valued more by those who make decisions about money. In academia, this can be seen through the funding of research projects, skewing certain disciplines and pushing research in particular directions. It would also compound any biases in the research funding system, for example, if it turned out that funders tend to slightly favour applications headed by male researchers. (They do.) More often, it happens in relation to the different aspects of academic work, with research valued above teaching, since researchers are often paid more than teachers. The third pillar of the academic workload, administrative work, fares even worse than teaching, until at some mysterious tipping point it becomes the most valuable (the best paid) of all. Again, this value system is deeply connected with existing power structures, with women and minorities often over-represented in teaching-heavy roles, while they are always under-represented in the more senior, usually more research-focused, roles.

This sort of financial ranking starts to discipline us, as workers and as people, but it is far from the only discipline mechanism that money generates. Precarity limits your options in multiple ways, from narrowing your focus to building your CV, becoming ever more competitive in an increasingly competitive job market, to taking up your thinking time with budgeting and anxiety. Even if you try to resist it, as I definitely did, being on the job market forces you to think of yourself in terms of money, as I definitely do. We are encouraged to list the financial amounts of any grants or awards on our CV, so prospective employers can tot up our worth. I have become deeply aware of how much 'value' I could bring to a prospective university, and I'm well practiced in describing myself this way.

Even those in stable or permanent roles face challenges with money, with a recent study[1] (done by an employers' association no less) showing that university staff in the UK have faced a decline in their pay of about 17 per cent since 2009. In particular, this means that those who have started work in the sector since then may never catch up to the earnings of those who started even a few years previous. Worst of all, this is happening when the cost of attending university is increasing. Students arrive on campus fully aware of the money they are committing to the institution. These students will graduate into debt that will shape their working lives, their sense of value. It shapes their choices at university as well, playing no small part in the rising mental health crisis for university students—a crisis that is rivalled by that amongst staff. One of the strangest experiences in teaching and advising students is when they look for career advice: they are looking for guidance towards stability and a route out of that debt, and perhaps the most honest thing I could say would be not to do what I did.

The background to all of this is an overall surplus for higher education in the UK of over 2 billion pounds in 2018, leading students and academics to wonder, whenever they take a break from worrying about money, what exactly is it that is being valued?

—Muireann O'Dwyer

[1] https://ucu.org.uk/article/10342/Value-of-university-staff-pay-has-plummeted-in-last-decade-employers-own-research-reveals?list=1676

€$£ €$£ €$£

TRAVELLING BY FERRY AND TRAIN via London and Paris I eventually arrived in Madrid. It was 1989, I was twenty, and I took this cumbersome method solely for the symbolism of it, thinking of my literary heroes—Orwell, Auden, Spender, and Isherwood—who had travelled the Continent by train and ferry in the 1930s. In this small way I could emulate them, I who had aspirations to write when I was in Spain.

I chose to take a long stopover in London, during which I met my girlfriend who made it clear that she would not, after all, be following me on to Spain. This was contrary to our former plan, which had been to spend a year living together in Madrid teaching English as a foreign language in local academies there, and to write in our spare time. Because in the few short weeks since I had seen her last in Dublin, she had met someone new in London, moved in with them, and become my ex-girlfriend.

Consequently I travelled on, alone, to spend a year by myself in the Spanish capital. Perhaps, I consoled myself, this isolation would inspire me to write more while there.

When I was collected by my new employer at Atocha Train Station, I was driven directly out of the city, far out, to a dusty and remote satellite town, little more than a series of apartment blocks situated around even dustier plazas, far from the urban centre of Madrid itself.

This was the site of the English Academy I had been employed to teach in, the classes taking place on the ground floor of one of the apartment buildings, the accommodation for the teachers located above.

A month previously I had, along with my then-girlfriend and several other aspirant teachers, sat a weekend-long TEFL course in Dublin, at the end of which we had all been handed a manual including the addresses and phone numbers of language academies in Spain; after phoning as many of these as I could before guilt at the charges I was racking up on my father's phone bill got to me, I had secured this job: Teaching English in an Academy I had thought would be in the city.

I had great plans: to wander the Retiro and sip *café con leche* in pavement cafés; to visit the Prado and consider great works of art; to write in the ancient bars of the Latin Quarter.

But there was nothing of interest in this satellite town I had ended up in, and there was consequently little to do during the work-week. I dutifully delivered the classes to the groups of children who turned up every day, went to a bar in the evenings and chatted with the other teachers, then returned to my room and slept. Writing was still but an aspiration in the stifling doldrums of this dusty town I was stranded in; and I told myself I would begin at the weekend, and then finally figure out a routine.

It was not the life I had anticipated; not the life of an Orwell or Isherwood.

At the end of that first week, however, about to go up to my apartment and change out of my teaching clothes into something more casual, I was met by my employer, the Director of the Academy, who ushered me curtly into her office and summarily dismissed me from my position.

This was unexpected.

Admittedly I was not a particularly skilled EFL teacher, having just about absorbed enough information from my weekend TEFL course to pass my weekend TEFL course exam and so obtain my weekend TEFL course Certificate of Competence. But no one else in the Academy was any more qualified than I was, as far as I could tell, and I had been under the impression that the job I had been doing was an adequate one. Turning up on time neat in my jacket and tie, the only teacher in the Academy to be so attired, delivering the grammar and vocabulary drills with as much precision as I could muster, keeping the kids firmly in line—I felt I was, at least, a passable EFL teacher.

The issue, however, was with the children, not me; or rather, it was with me. Because it turned out that the kids were not sitting in class in rapt attention as I had supposed, but rather in terror. They were, quite simply, afraid of me and my stern, formal demeanour. I had neglected to appreciate that with these kids, all under the age of ten, my main role, and aim, was to be a baby-sitter, to molly-coddle and amuse them. In reality, the kids were in tears at the thought of being subjected to my teaching, and throwing tantrums at the prospect of having to attend my classes.

Despite pleading that I would ditch the jacket and tie, lighten up, and generally change my demeanour to one that could be deemed more child-friendly, the Director stood firm: I was fired, and had to go, immediately, which meant vacating the apartment also.

That day I moved all my belongings via the ancient and unreliable local train from the satellite town into the centre of Madrid, where I found a room in a city centre pensión easily enough.

Then, with my money running low, and having now to pay for accommodation where previously it had been free, I started to look for a new job. This involved phoning as many academies as possible, on payphones or from the telephone exchange, the Telefónica. But it was late in the season, and the schools were no longer looking for teachers.

Days passed, then a week, and my funds began to grow precipitously low. Any hopes I had of beginning to write were set aside as I faced the ongoing stress of getting by day-to-day while my money began to run out.

At a certain point I calculated that I now had enough to either pay for my fare home or stay for another week's job-hunting. Not wanting to face the humiliation of returning home in failure so soon after my departure, or the even greater humiliation of asking someone for a loan, I decided to take a chance, and continued looking for a job.

Now, constantly stressed, I recalled how I had left Ireland for Spain, not so long before, full of plans and ideals.

That day, my father had driven me to the ferry port in Dún Laoghaire. It was dusk, darkening already, the end of summer, and I was taking the night sailing to Holyhead. We sat in the car in the darkness without speaking, waiting for the time to arrive for me to embark. We had not spoken much in the previous weeks or indeed months; not about my recent graduation from college, nor about the time I'd just spent working in London, nor about my plans for the future and my intention to write. Indeed, as always, we had hardly spoken much at all.

I had no idea what he was thinking or feeling as he prepared to see his only son set off into the unknown; for it was the unknown to him because I had given him scant details of my intentions.

But just as I was about to get out of the car and go into the terminal, he leaned over to the glove compartment, opened it, took something out and handed it to me. Examining it in the dim glow of the overhead streetlights I saw it was a wad of banknotes: a roll of pesetas, enough to get me through several weeks living in Spain, given to me unasked for.

It was as it had always been: he could not say what he wished to say to me in words, but with a kind gesture could speak profoundly of what he was feeling.

In Madrid, my endless phone calls finally paid off. Within a week, my money just lasting, I was able to secure another job, the Director of this new Academy paying me cash at the end of the first week so that within a short amount of time I once more had enough to get by, and support myself.

But for that short period when I was out of work with funds ever-dwindling, unsure of what to do and facing the dismal prospect of returning home, I like to think that it was my father's gift of pesetas that ensured I could remain in Madrid and finally begin to write.

—Arnold Thomas Fanning

€$£ €$£ €$£

THIS YEAR, I AM 'MONEY WRITING'.

Fiction writing takes time (for me, anyway) which is why I have been self-employed most of my adult life, taking work on a job-by-job basis, fitting it around book-writing and child-rearing, and turning it down when I can afford to.

By the time my last book came out, finances were not good. Accompanying the general publication come-down (the realisation that your book is just-another-book like everybody else's) was a terrible shame at having asked so much of my partner while I 'got the book right', and of failing to properly provide for our family for well over two years.

So, I vowed to put aside 'creative writing' for a while, and concentrate on 'money writing'. This means that instead of spending all day writing-and-deleting, or tinkering with three tricky sentences, I have been churning out 'eco copy' at exactly 350 words per hour.

Mostly, I write brochures and case studies. The work is basically propaganda for those I consider the good guys—scientists trying to stave off climate change; sociologists trying to support 'socially fair' policy. This often involves using the words 'stakeholders', 'key players', and other such linguistic duds: a special kind of torture for a writer.

In any discussion about art and material circumstances, Virginia Woolf's 'A Room of One's Own' will likely be hovering. In her essay, Woolf lists the material needs that must be met in order for women to be able to write. The essay emphasises the importance of 'the rich yellow flame of rational conversation,' and how poor food and accommodation can mire it.

Of course, poorly fed, poorly sheltered people with no privacy are not in a prime position to write; people who were never taught to read are not in a position to write; people working double shifts are not in a position to write. To believe it's all an equal playing field is to perpetuate all kinds of terrible isms.

But I think there is another subtle danger at play too, in the idea that the petty concerns of the material world are inconducive to fiction writing. It characterises the writer as a bit of a 'brain in the bag', as though great literature can only come from the writer-brain disentangled from unpleasant little distractions like a bad meal.

As humans we are in a terrible bind between acknowledging our materiality and striving for some greater 'meaning', and isn't that where art always starts? The old notion of art-as-sublime is based on the idea that by creating an encounter with death, artistic work leads the viewer/reader to catharsis and self-transcendence.

This feeds into the idea of the pure, transcendent-mind-writer, but undercuts it as well. It is only with the body—the confrontation with mortality—that art has any function. Surely, we must write from the body and all its experiences?

When I told my boss—or rather, a friend who subs work to me—that I was trying to find the time to write something about money and writing, she e-mailed back: 'It seems to me the more interesting the work, the less it pays, and vice versa.'

This might explain why I have never been paid as much for 300 words of fiction, as I have for 'Five catchy sub-heads with engaging 50-word blurbs on project achievements'.

One difference between writing paid copy and writing fiction is that the first is overtly pushing an agenda; but the purpose of literature is not always even clear to me. Part purge, part prayer—I am not entirely sure what the 'writerly' act is, other than the only psychic survival method that has ever done me right.

As both a cultural act and a personal operation, art functions much like religion in that, for both an individual and a society, fictional narrative is the only way to make sense of the mortal world. It gives the semblance of sense or justice to the amorphous nonsense of experience; it imbues life with 'meaning'.

That is not to denigrate art—I think it is part of the human condition. But trade is often cited as another mark of civilisation. The relationship between these two very human traits is, I suppose, at the heart of the 'money and writing' conundrum.

*

I used Arts Council bursaries to write my last two books. In practical terms, this is a lump of money that represents a concrete excuse not to do 'money writing' for a while, and to use that time to write books instead. These bursaries are a way of 'supporting diversity' (to glean a term from my money writing), on the grounds that if 'interesting' writing simply doesn't pay, then the only ones writing it will be those materially rich enough not to need it to, and probably those without dependents.

These support-the-arts payments are based on the idea that commercially unviable pursuits have a cultural value that is worth some very small portion of the state's money. In a liberal capitalist world, a thing's value is determined by what people will pay to consume it; what role it performs in the economic system. I am genuinely unsure whether what is meant by 'cultural value' is something outside this economy, or a more complex part of it. Is it, for example, to do with tourism, or the education industry?

To write *Down and Out in Paris and London* George Orwell played at being poor. He lived in near destitution and worked in poorly paid jobs, but knowing he had a home he could return to when things got too bad he could never actually access the experience. His identification remained hypothetical. He was always documenting the experiences of others.

One of America's greatest short story writers, Lucia Berlin, never really achieved commercial success due to financial restraints and alcoholism. Inspired by her experiences working as a cleaning lady, a nurse, and an alcoholic mother, she did, however, produce some of the most wonderful short stories I have ever read.

While a writer's life is, of course, far more comfortable with a room of one's own, simply having access to 'the right circumstances to write' will not produce the kind of work that derives from engagement with the real world, the world of material constraints, and the world of work.

—Elske Rahill

In the beginning
        there is this small place

and in it is
        everything

and in the end
        it is
                nothing

it is
        no where

if facts were truth
        there would be no need
                for

Truth and meaning are
        not

getting closer to

Taking this tablet
this is war

Not taking this tablet
this is war

Having to take this tablet
this is war

Not having to take this tablet
this is war

Being told to take this tablet
this is war

Being forced to take this tablet
this is war

Being stopped from taking this tablet
this is war

When Power makes decisions
this is war

When Power neglects to make decisions
this is war

this part of you
we're going to take it away
and put it over here
and call it love

Eating this Pizza
here
this is war

This brand
this can of orange juice
this is war

This bland thought
this morning television
this is war

'Can I just have some Somosas
I'll pay for them on Monday'
this is war

these Chemicals
these bees
this is war

This News
this Make-Up
this is war

These babies
these babies
this is war

Smile
smile
this is war

this eye
this ear
this tongue this gaze
this is war

this home

this is war

weains out animals fed washing on
dishes done sticky plasters all   this is

the sounds of an approaching car
its pace
        its timbre
                this is war
an echo ■■■■
■■■ windscreens
■■ hummm
■■■■■■ engine■ ■■■■■
knowing
■■ not looking ■■■■■
■■■ is war

while away
        while away
                while away
                        this is war
our kitchen tap squeals
when you let the water out
somewhere between pain and whale

this routine
verb
noun
attaching light to dark

this inadequacy
this knowledge
this is ■■■

~~she~~ came ~~she~~ said
out of love
I believe ~~her~~
~~she~~ stayed ~~she~~ said out of   war
love
I believe ~~her~~
~~she~~ told the stories of those
whose stories were not
being told
I believe ~~her~~
~~she~~ wrote to ~~herself~~ about
~~herself~~ and what it would be
like and that it would be
alright
I believe ~~her~~
~~she~~ stood at night witness to
the world being the world
I believe ~~her~~
After giving a talk about
thinking and how to get to
somewhere where there is
no path to we went to a bar
for a drink which I rarely do
and at that moment   song
elsewhere in that moment
they shot ~~her~~ so believe me
this is ■■■

Kakangelism

The worst is coming, it always must.
You have been living in an interlude.
It is a wave you can hear if you listen,
it has been racing towards you all your life.
It was there at the back of your vision,
at the moment you first slumped into existence,
backbeat to the most graceful flight you ever had,
the one time you hit top B in public,
pinched tight into the sublimest of paintings,
vibrating under the choral depths
as a dark undertone of snarling menace
in your brightest ideas, your freshest phrases.
When you kissed on that one summer night,
your entire life seemingly distilled
into something approximating sense,
it was there underneath the lake's soft breathing,
somehow within the touch of her linen dress.
Infants hear it keening and point to it,
dogs whimper as it strengthens after dusk.
It warps the firmest reality effect,
the most profound sensory foundations,
corrupting all your necessary machines
with the foretaste of eventual deluge.

Graham Allen

Night Philosopher

Hugo Kelly

It was a Saturday night that I first heard about the whale on Midwest Radio. The creature had beached itself near Ormay Island. It's very shallow out there and if it didn't find the right channel it would be stuck on one of the sandbars that farmers use to go back and forth to the islands at low tide.

Joan, my other half, was asleep and the house was quiet except for the radio. We'd been out earlier in the evening with Ron and Anya, celebrating his birthday. After we'd ordered, Anya chattered to the waiter in Lithuanian for about fifteen minutes. Joan played with her drink and looked bored. She's doing a course in rural development and doesn't go out much these days. She doesn't like Anya much either.

Outside the wind had picked up, and a rush of rain pelted like spikes against the blue glass. Some tail-end of a hurricane from the Caribbean with a doll's name was stroking the west coast. The horizon darkened to the colour of graphite. It was early August but I was already thinking of autumn.

The waiter left at last and there was a lull in the conversation.

'You know it's ten years tonight since Phil Codey killed himself,' Joan suddenly said.

Ron sat back and slugged from his pint.

'You're right,' he said as if it had been a question. 'Around the bank holiday as far as I remember.'

'Yeah,' she said emphatically. 'It's ten years.'

'Who is Phil Codey?' Anya asked.

'He was this guy who used to work nights with us in the factory years ago. He committed suicide,' Ron said.

'Why did he kill himself?' Anya asked.

Ron looked at me. I shrugged my shoulders.

'I think he was depressed,' Ron said. 'Who knows about these things?'

'Was he a gay?' she asked.

Ron started laughing. But it was a nervous laugh.

'What has that got to do with anything?' Joan said.

'I had a cousin who committed suicide,' Anya said. 'He was a gay.'

She looked daggers at Joan.

'Codey was different, a special person,' Joan said. 'He had a hard time growing up but he found this way of looking at the world, a kind of wisdom I suppose. He could quote these beautiful things. It was an awful shock what happened.'

'My cousin was very clever as well,' Anya retorted. 'He was studying to be a doctor.'

On it went like that; Joan talking about Codey and the old days when we worked on the line; Anya sniping at her; Ron smiling uncomfortably as he knocked back the pints; me dreaming of our pre-ordered taxi.

On the way home I said to Joan: 'You know Anya may not be the most sophisticated person, but we have to get on with her.'

'She's a fool,' Joan said. 'The two of them are well matched.'

As the taxi slowed to a halt, I leaned into her and whispered, 'You know, Joan, just because you're doing a distance degree in rural development that doesn't make you a better person.'

'You're probably correct about that,' she said. 'But you're just bothered that it might.'

There were more words between us later and then she went to bed. I stayed up, listening to Midwest Radio, looking at my reflection in the conservatory window. Some local expert said it was a sperm whale, a young male, small for its age and probably sick. No one is really sure why they beach like that but chances are that this one just got lost, confused amongst all the islands that dot the bay like stepping stones. Given the whale's weak condition, there wasn't anything that could be done.

Outside the wind dragged at the glass and the roof tiles so that the house creaked and groaned. I imagined the heavy water of the harbour with its spoiled, silty look, pulling and shunting under the attention of the storm. A foul taste filled my mouth.

That's how Phil Codey did it. Basically he drove his ten-year-old Toyoto Igo off the quay wall into the bay. It was eleven o'clock at night and there were a few people about near the apartments. They ran to the quay side and saw the car, piece of tin that it was, still floating on the slimy water. Slowly the current turned the car around until it faced the quayside. And there was Codey looking out at everyone. They screamed at him, begged him to get out. But Codey just stared into the middle distance as if waiting at a traffic light. The car tilted as it went down. And then Codey was gone.

I took out my mobile and called Ron. He answered straight away.

'Hey,' he said.

'Sorry', I said. 'The night didn't go to plan.'

'Yeah,' he said. 'Anya's in a mood now. Not much of a birthday in the end.'

I think he was getting at Joan but I decided not to go there.

'Joan's still thinking about Codey. I didn't expect that,' I said.

I could hear Ron dragging heavily on a cigarette.

'That's all in the past,' he exhaled. 'Codey was always going to end badly. Some people are marked.'

That was cruel, even for Ron, but I moved on.

'Did you hear about the whale on Midwest?' I asked.

'I did.'

'He's a young guy. I wonder is there a chance that he might get back into the channel?'

Ron didn't seem to hear me. Listening isn't one of his skills.

'They'll have to get rid of it, which won't be easy. I suppose they could bury it. Otherwise it'll stink for miles around.'

'He's not dead yet,' I said.

'Would they ever blow it up?' he continued. 'Get the army in. But then you'd have rotting blubber everywhere. Still the seagulls would be happy.'

'Listen,' I said. 'What if we tried to move the whale back into the channel. We could call to Bill. He's got the boat and ropes and all that stuff.'

Ron sighed.

'Bill is away on the boats,' he said. 'You won't get him.'

'But… we could still get some of his stuff. From the shed like we used to when we went out fishing.'

'Let it rest,' he said, 'We've had a few drinks and it's been a long night. We can't do anything for a whale stranded in the middle of nowhere.'

'That's you,' I said, 'Never willing to even try.'

'You've been cranky all night,' he said. 'Go to bed.'

He hung up then and I didn't feel any better. It's not a good sign when Ron comes across as the more mature person.

On the radio the whale was already the last line of the local news, fading into the death notices. For a moment I half expected them to mention Phil Codey. But in truth not many people would remember him. I looked in the direction of the sea, lost as it was in the soupy darkness, and thought of the whale out there, stranded and confused in the storm. Maybe that's when I decided. It's hard to know.

In the hallway I picked up the jeep keys from the table. I thought about leaving a note or something for Joan, but I didn't. Outside the wind was howling and it was good to get out of the house. It was good to feel I was doing something.

It didn't take me long to get to Bill's house. It lay there shaded grey against the dark fields. Bill was one of our gang that worked nights, putting tubes of contact lens solution into boxes that went around the world. We were young and immature, making money at last. They were good times. Nowadays he does boat trips out on the bay for tourists and then some working on the trawlers. I don't know what he does in the winter. He's turned into one of those people who gets by. I went around the back to a couple of sheds that he keeps his bits and pieces in. The door had a rusty padlock for show that I knew opened with a bit of force. When I got in I saw Bill's fibreglass fifteen-footer, sitting there already on the trailer, its best days over. But I knew it would do. These times they have special inflatable pontoon yokes for rescuing whales and dolphins, ones that grip them underneath and on either side. I saw it on a documentary last year. Then they just float them out to sea. I couldn't lay my hands on anything like that but maybe if I caught the tide turning, the deeper water might give the whale some buoyancy so that I could pull it back into the channel where the water is deep. That was the plan anyway. I located some strips of sail canvas and a couple of coiled ropes. I opened the garage door and pulled out the boat, putting back the useless lock before I left.

It took me almost an hour to get out to Ormay. After twenty miles the road begins to turn and curve in on itself like a ball of wool. Above me the mountain hid in the darkness like a bad memory. I tried not to think about

Phil Codey, but there he was, this scrawny boy in a grubby shirt and jumper reeking of neglect. Maybe Ron was right: maybe he was marked. Once the two of us had to undress together as part of the examination by the Public Health Nurse doing her school check-up. As he pulled down his trousers I saw that he wore no underpants. As soon as we were out I told everyone, and he was nicknamed *Knickers* after that. I never mentioned the bruises that I saw because I didn't understand them. He dropped out of school at fourteen. No one tried to bring him back.

Years later, out of the blue, Codey turned up in the factory. He had spent a few years in England and came back a new person. He read books aloud in the canteen, spouting about Plato and Kahlil Gibran, quoting from this and that. The 'Night Philosopher' they called him, which of course he loved. It was when he started to dole out advice that he got annoying.

There was one final, terrible bend in the road and suddenly the strand opened in front of me. It was narrow and deep like the mouth of a river, the white sand travelling out in the darkness of the bay towards the off-shore islands. The wind was still roaring but the sky was clear except for the few rag-shaped clouds that blew past. I could see the car tracks scraped along the sand, winding over the shallow, glistening streams where earlier someone had already been out to the stranded whale.

I drove on, travelling around the headland towards the island. It wasn't long until the lights of the jeep picked out the shape, a dark mark on the sand. Soon I could see the blockish frame that curved like a spoon to the wide tailfin. Already it appeared damaged, like a deflating balloon. A thin veil of water flowed around it. The jeep shuddered as I came to a halt.

I opened the car door, leaving the lights on, and inhaled the fermented salty air. Not far off the water in the channel appeared black and treacly in the darkness. Now I could see that the whale's skin was a steel grey as it lay curved in front of me. I stepped closer, tremors prickling along my legs. There was a pungent odour tainting the air as if death was being exhaled from the porous sand underfoot.

I forced myself to stop and stare at the creature. The block head travelled down through its body to the squat dorsal fin where knuckles of bone ran along its spine. It was long yet not bulky, so despite its size it looked young and underdeveloped. I could make out circular plug shapes dotted across its frame; attack marks of some sort, I guessed. On the pendulum-like tail I saw a raw patch, an open wound, perhaps an ulcer. And then underneath its bulk its distended penis peeped out sad and slack against the sand. As I walked around it I caught a glimpse of white at its head, a blinking eye that looked out forlornly just above the thin water line. Its jaw trembled and a thin trail of blood seeped from the corner of its mouth, dissipating into the water. It sensed me close by.

The wind died down momentarily, and in the quiet I could pick out murmurs and strange whispers as its being slowly extinguished. I knew then that there was nothing that could be done, if ever there had been. I reached out and placed the palm of my hand on its sloped head. Its skin was cold, like damp scuffed leather, yet there was a give, the resolute softness of flesh. The moon slipped in behind the broken clouds. Rain slanted in from the sea. The wind whipped foam from the waves. The white eye blinked again and then blankness.

I sat back in the jeep and lay my head on the steering wheel, suddenly exhausted. The wind pushed hard. I heard a slosh of water and lifted my head. The tide had turned in the interval and water was sliding past the wheels. Again I thought of Codey and how he died. I wondered then as I always did whether Joan knew what we had done to him all those years ago in the warehouse. It was just a prank that got out of hand. Maybe a warning to keep to himself with his wisdom.

I sat there while the seawater ebbed back and forth around the jeep. Outside the wind howled and spun like a demon drawing breath. Minutes drifted by. The water was coming in fast. Already I could see the whale's tail fin was partially submerged as the sea rose. A tall wave exploded around it, covering the body. The sea was taking him back. And in that instant I felt the sea reach out to me, a kindly offer like a journey's end. The waves rolled in thick, blustering motions towards me. The jeep began to creak and vibrate at their impact. Wispy foam blew onto the windscreen so that already I felt that I was submerged.

I don't remember turning the key but the noise of the spluttering engine pulled me back. It coughed and spat, nearly giving out, but my foot found the accelerator and I revved until the engine began to smoke oily fumes. I drove slowly through the rising tide, turning away from the grey horizon as the water cascaded either side of me. At last I reached the beach again and retraced the miles I had come.

By the time I reached our house, dawn was pushing through on the horizon. There were no lights on and I knew that I hadn't been missed. Once inside I walked down through the shadows of the hallway to the bedroom. I peered in and looked at Joan sleeping. She lay neat and composed, lost in dreams. I wanted to go and sit beside her, perhaps softly wake her as if I were a returned soldier; someone anxiously awaited. But I didn't carry good news like that. Instead I could still taste salt in my mouth, could feel the damp rub of my wet clothes. The light of dawn filtered into the room and I turned and walked back along the corridor towards the other bedroom.

I lay on the bed and closed my eyes, searching for the ease of sleep, but in my mind's eye all I could see was the spoiled sea and the whale beached in its shallows. I knew that I would have to tell Joan about Codey and what had happened. And so I lay there listening to the hiss and gasps of the waves as they shunted towards me like the coming days.

Precedence

The trams still run on time
people still lie in the sun
on our backs in a room
a stack of books is a home

we can still walk in and out
of galleries and look at the sky
and think it is a paint shade
of blue you have waited to see

in the city where the trams still
run and we greet each other
with smiles and greet each other
with smiles while the trams still

run our hands are not too tight
in each other's and what precedence
has this day over any other
we have lived in the cold

where the cold kept us pacing
and our lips moving and your lips
moving your hand at your ear
where your blood echoes the blue

could be winter blue where
the ice grows grounding
the town the river beneath
still seething where nothing

appears to move it is moving
as we are moving in the coarse
light of the tram in the coarse
moving light of the tram

Leeanne Quinn

Sea Eagle Sonata

Niamh MacCabe

ask him if he'd like a top-up

        customers don't generally get top-ups for tea, top-ups are for coffee only, you know that, he knows that, tea is a once-off thing, a beginning a middle an end kind of thing, a ritual cup in your hand, it has parameters and limits beyond which it cannot and will not—

shut up / just go out there and ask him / he looks wrecked / more wrecked than usual

The elderly baker sticks his head through the hanging beads separating kitchen from café. It's early morning; the place is empty but for the young man sitting at a table by the window, scrolling through his phone.

'Would you like a top-up for your tea there?'

'Eh, I, I'm grand, thanks.'

'Thought so. Maybe a drop of hot water? Or hot water and another teabag? Or is that just a new tea altogether? Haha! Like, when does the old cup actually become a new cup? Or is a cup of tea the tea or the cup? Haha! Wild stuff.'

'Yeah, I'm grand, thanks a mill.'

he doesn't want to chat / look at the state of him / don't overstep the mark

'Look, I'll leave you alone, never mind me, I'm an awful man for rambling on, as you well know by now!'

'No worries, sham.'

'If you need a top-up, just shout. I'll be foostering around, as usual, thinking up poems with me big flowery apron on, haha!'

'Sound.'

go back into the kitchen will you / sort out the eclairs

'Or I'll be in the kitchen sorting out eclairs and things. Shout if you change your mind about the top-up.'

quit talking about top-ups / the eclairs are beginning to curl up in the oven

'Anyways, righto, I'm off, son. Back shortly.'

for the love of God don't call him son

'Grand. Thanks.'

The young man draws his chair closer in to the table, takes wireless headphones from his jacket pocket, places them over his ears, turns back to his phone. The baker returns to the windowless kitchen, sits on a stool by the warm oven, puts his head in his hands.

christ, did you see his face, poor lad, eyes like piss-holes

yes

should have left him in peace, that's what he comes in here for

and stop with the bloody origami swans

yes, should quit folding doily birds for him, he's not a damn child, he's getting handy at them though, remember yesterday morning's attempt, nearly there, but the wee wings were fecked, we'll work on that today, are the buns baked

eclairs / they are

good

listen / something's up with that youngster

I always listen, should I take them eclairy-buns out

so you do / yes take them out

I do mostly because you never shut up, put the cream on is it

wait till they cool / start whipping the cream / microwave the chocolate

wouldn't shut up when you were with me, won't shut up now, wait till they cool then dollop cream into them and slap some chocolate on, it's grand, it'll be grand, I'll be fine

you'll be fine / you're doing great

am I now, am I, I can see your beautiful hands doing it great

don't / no point

and your arms white with flour, the hairs standing up on them with the cold from the door open onto the morning, you were some handsome woman

no point remembering

and the odd stroller walking by with a dog or a bike or a child, gawking in, smelling the hot sweetness—

what's the point

—and after, like nothing happened, you decorating the cakes, all business—

nothing happening

—bent over the trays, tongue tipping out the side of your mouth, squeezing the sweet cream from some rubbery triangle thing

the pastry bag

the rubber yoke like a mini-set of uilleann pipes, cream swirling from its plastic chanter reed onto the cakes and the buns and the everything

pointless / I'm gone

you were something else

I was

us locking fingers and spinning round the floor together like a mad gyroscope—

a gyroscope is it

—at night when the shutters were down, not letting go till we hit the ground

room swirling behind us

the eyes reeling in our heads, the spiralling

wild whirlwinds

the two of us, two and a bit

two and a chance

one minus one-and-a-half leaves negative equity

…

hard to believe, to get used to, where are you gone

where

where is that pastry lung-bag thing

in the cutlery drawer

I miss you

yes

seven months eleven days, hard to get used to, two hundred and
twenty-six days

you need to talk to people

who are you telling

to real people

I know

to that young man / as troubled as he is

yes

open up

yes

without whinging

okay

he could do with it too

probably

a bit of warmth / of kindness

how can I talk to people when all I hear is you warbling on about
kindness and cream

don't forget to turn the oven off

yes

whip sugar into the cream

righto

gently / you're not flailing a dead pony

it's flogging a dead horse

make some dark and some milk chocolate / the young go for the darker

yes

don't call him son / he's somebody's son / but he's not ours

not ours indeed

no

ours with the teeny flat lungs sealed inside its ribcage, parcelled up
inside you, inside a box, inside the ground—

*stop / talk appropriate talk to him / talk about climate change / rise of
the alt-right / social media*

or origami, the origins of—

or the lad's computery job / something's wrong there

something's not right

talk to him / you used to be good with people

if you say so

bring eclairs / one dark one milk

The baker places a white doily on a plate and arranges two eclairs on it. He
picks up a tiny origami swan from a collection above the oven and places it
on the tray beside the plate. He goes out to the young man, who is staring out

the window, headphones slung around his neck, his back to the kitchen, some flaking gold-lettered football club insignia stretching from shoulder blade to thin shoulder blade.

'Here we are! Straight from the oven! On the house this time, my friend!'

'Eh, well, thanks. You're good to me.'

don't sit / too much / put down the plate

'Cripes, but you've been working hard! Ten-hour shifts, through the night—'

he'll think you're a stalker

'—don't worry, I'm no stalker! It's just that I spot you going in across the road…'

a stalker then

'… heading up the stairwell before the time-delay light switch turns off… because, you see, I'm in for a wee while at night to set the oven for morning.'

'Are you? You're as bad as me so.'

'Sourdough, ciabatta, multigrain, the lot. Fistful of pumpkin seeds on everything. Swift learning curve for this here gent! The missus…'

don't bring me up

'… You see, the missus used to do it all.'

The young man leans back in his chair, zips his sports jacket up to his chin, sinks his mouth in behind the polyester, stuffs his hands in the pockets.

'Yeah, there was a missus, believe it or not... And then, you see, when I'm back in the morning, I do watch you emerging bleary-eyed from across the way. Fair play to you, fair play.'

'It's not too bad, really. It's grand.'

'Look, I'm getting you a fresh cup, back in a sec. Here's another little paper bird for you while you're waiting, have a go again at copying it. You're doing good. Trick is, start by figuring out how it's made. Unfold this one first. Work backwards. Then make it again. And dig in to the eclairs, get some meat on those bones!'

'I will, thanks.'

The young man leans forward in his chair, places his elbows on the table, rests his chin in one hand and gives a weary thumbs-up with the other. As the baker returns to the kitchen, he hears the young man's phone ping. He looks back through the beads. The man checks his phone, winces, places it in his pocket, unzips his jacket halfway, and picks up the origami swan. He stares at it for a while, rotating it in his palm, then returns it to the table. He straightens his back and with his mouth hanging open rubs both eyes with closed fists, like a child, before picking up the swan again. The baker's breath catches in his throat, and he turns back quickly to his kitchen, sits once more by the oven.

meat-on-bones was not appropriate

didn't bother him, think he likes the attention

maybe

look at him, head bent to the folded swan

he's spent from work

imagine sitting in an open-plan office all night, everyone lined up in front of screens

all night

imagine having to decide what's right and what's wrong for the rest of us babbys, that's a woeful amount of pressure for a young lad, barely a man, a woeful amount of badness to take on

it is

he's a good lad, it's not fair, some of the things he's had to watch, the few he's told me, remember

don't

can't get some of them out of my head

no, don't

like the young prisoner backed up to a black flag with white script, hands tied with barbed wire behind him, ordered to kneel in a language he doesn't understand, fuck sakes, why

bad to dwell here

somebody's son

think of the two of us / think of two and a chance

chance, him on the top floor across the way working all night while
the two of us are sleeping, or at least while I am and you, you
hollowy willowy thing, curled up around the half-bit in my dreams

still in your dreams

do you dream, a dream dreaming

don't get upset / you're doing great

am I

the tea / bring him his tea

The baker returns to the young man, who is now texting. The eclairs are gone.

'Here you go, my friend, a top-up in your hand whether you ordered it or not! That's the sort of me! Can't bear to see a man with a cold cup. Well now, you've unfolded the bird but it can't be said you've put it back together again, now can it! Haha, you're flummoxed, as smart as you are! Flummoxed by a wee paper bird!'

'You're right there, sham! I'm a bit of an eejit sometimes! Me head's all over the place. Enjoying this tea, though, it's hitting the spot. Thanks.'

check the milk

'Plenty of milk in the jug for you. You're no eejit. Now, drink up! And take your time. Morning traffic beginning to build outside, where are they all rushing to? And they'll all rush back this evening. Work, work, work.'

'Work, work, work, and more work. It's all a balls, to be fair. That's the truth. Sorry for the language. I'm fucking wrecked. I'll be grand by this evening.'

ask him about time off

'Do you get much holidays? Time to clear the mind of all that online muck heaped on you? Head off anywhere nice? With the missus...'

don't start talking about a missus / you should know better

'... or even by yourself? I spent a set of days on the Isle of Skye, seven months ago now it must have been. All on me ownio, dodging the seagulls, walking the hills and the hollows by the shore. Fecking beautiful, pardon mon french. Just me and the gulls. Or the gulls and I, as someone would have corrected me, once. Wait till I see, I think I have the box of pics here in the kitchen somewhere.'

Something about the old baker's holiday pictures; the shoddiness of the paper, the fading colours, the occasional fat corner-thumb, the blurred seagulls in flight. Something about the lopsided selfies, the cut-off heads, about how sure the baker was that these limp, bleached photographs of the Isle of Skye would somehow be meaningful to me. And something about the picture of a large black solitary rock silhouetted on a headland jutting out to an edgeless sea, with the words THE BLACK ROCK written in red felt-tip pen below. Something about all that steered me.

I didn't go home to my bed in Flatland. I took the Luas to Connolly Station, bought a ticket for the Belfast Enterprise. Slept on the train. Swallowed hot sweet tea on the ferry to Stranraer, milky coffee on the train to Glasgow. Flicked through my phone at Premier League results and fixtures until the battery died, then stared through my strobed reflection out at the plunging black night as I was scuttled over the tracks to Inverness. By the time I made it to a Kyle of Lochalsh dawn, I had run out of my cache of sterling.

I walked, hunched into spring drizzle, across the bridge to the Isle of Skye. Fat seagulls muttered and hobbled a criss-cross in front of me like they'd been waiting. The hood of my Sligo Football Club jacket was tied tight against the damp morning air. I knew this weather. No one was around to read the county's motto arched across my shoulders, Land Of Heart's Desire, the once-gold lettering fading back into the striped black and white polyester. 'Heart's Desire calling, my friends and people,' I told the gulls.

A lone taxi appeared. I described the black rock I'd seen in the baker's photograph.

'Ah, Scorrybreac,' he said, and took a twenty euro note to drop me to a carpark in Portree Bay, with instructions on how to reach the headland from there.

As I climbed the trail, rocky seashore on my right, the sun came out. I thought of my job; how the other content moderators would probably have covered for me last night, though the quick staff turnover meant some of them don't even know my name. I thought of my stale half-litre of milk sitting in the staff fridge beside the energy drinks and granola bars, each item labelled with our own individual workstation numbers. I thought of our communal Polo mints, and how there is always a packet or two doing the rounds in the office. I thought of our tiny windowless staff-room; a microwave, a fridge, a table with chairs. I thought of the conversations around that table, telling each other in low voices what we had seen on screen, what we had decided against, holding back on some of the uglier stuff, unable to voice it. And I thought of the lonely baker. I wondered whether this morning's absence had yet been noted.

When his Black Rock jutted before me, I sat down on the damp heather, jacket in lap. I took a chocolate bar from a pocket and ate it, peeling strips of tin foil from the gloop and letting them sail away one by one on the breeze. I folded the purple wrapper into a tiny imperfect swan. Pleating the small paper wings upward, I flicked it over the cliff edge and watched the purple swan spiralling slowly towards the waves. When I lost sight of it, I looked out to sea, blinking at the new sun's eye.

––––––––

She soars on a thermal, talons tucked into her body. Her mate is behind, calling. The sleek finger-feathers at either end of her dark wingspan flicker upward in the soft wind. The Atlantic glistens below.

She twists her head and eyes her mate. Extending his talons in play, his white tail fans out to slow his flight. He beats his broad dun wings, twice, then glides once more. She folds one wing into herself, turning back swiftly to him. Meeting, they interlock talons and cartwheel downward together through the air. Wings lashing against the spin, their pale yellow eyes are fixed, sea and sky tumbling behind them.

They disentangle above the water. Swooping apart, their feathers skim the unsettled surface. After four shallow wingbeats over the waves, they tilt back towards each other. He rolls under, touching his talons to hers before scudding upwards. She follows, calling.

The cliff face looms. Their enduring eyrie of heather, juniper and salted driftwood nestles in a hollow there, moss and shell dregs lining the inside.

She spots motion on the headland, banks sharp towards it. Sunlight is catching thin strips carried swirling on the wind. She draws nearer, focuses on a man releasing shiny slivers into the air. Her eye follows the inert falling tin. Disinterested, she beats her wings to rise and steadies onto a thermal once more. Her mate follows, silent.

Returning her gaze to the lone man, she watches him flick a small purple shape from him. Half-closing one wing, she dives down towards the spiralling form. When close to her mark she establishes its futility but is driven to catch it in her beak before twisting away upward. Her tongue probes the sweet pleated paper. Rolling her eye back under its bony brow-ridge to the man exposed on the headland above their eyrie, she watches him getting to his feet, staring at her, mouth open, arms hanging, a tangle of black, white, and gold at his feet. He calls out and slowly raises his arms wide, empty palms up, fingers splayed, yielding a bare throat. Her waiting mate signals caution with a deep repetitive cry, and she swings back up towards his open-winged silhouette hovering dark before the sun. She circles around him, still hearing the fading serenade from the prone man below, then pirouettes skyward, her mate following, his curved beak open, hymnal sea air whispering as siren across their wings.

———————

where

                           where is that pastry lung-bag thing

in the cutlery drawer / you're doing great

                                      am I

you are

         us locking fingers and spinning round the floor together

                       like a mad gyroscope—

a gyroscope is it

         —at night when the shutters were down, not letting go

                     till we hit the ground

Pathways

'Nature has a patient ear'
—Wendell Berry

The window is clammy with dew, amber where the sun has struck
that corner of the house. The garden lies in shade like a lover left to thrash
in lies and flowerbeds, cold earth. The tips of the aspens are stealing
from sleep's dreamy web into helpless oxygen. Jackdaws cry
under visceral skies, erase the riptide of loneliness
that shadows our better nature. Weeds flutter in chimney pots
across a field of rooftops. Each house is a trove shining with possibility.

*

Shadows the length of a GAA pitch, an old clock towering under
the ripple of ivy. The grass is patchy as memory, gold with the windfall
of broken leaves. Stray limbs prove the yellow warning,
gales that scratched the glass all night. Blades of light, little miracles
of technicolour. What path are we taking? Whose meandering verges
are we being led by? Does it lead to safety? Fear is in the clear
understanding of not knowing anything but where to go for strong coffee.

*

In the park the light's a mesh, a tangle of briars and muddy thorn.
Crushed seed sustains the blow of wandering lost in life's momentum.
We leave the market tearing croissants, sipping peace in snatched silence.
Birds scuffle in the undergrowth, make our bodies come alive.
Allow that stipend of sky to embolden us like children, drawn down to the nub.
Something escapes our attention, makes us look where we'd never.
The heart of the matter is rough with life, coated in fur.

*

Impulse leads to a straight line drawn from A to B, blurry
with expectation. Open up the mind and those restrictions
pass for opportunity. The thick copse gives way to other clearings,
winter grass cooling our feet. Seen from above we forge a way
but at eye level the world's a hush of ears and cinnabars. Thoughts vanish.
All rises to greet the lone traveller, including rain-filled potholes
whose frictions open like portals. Nothing is predictable or certain.

*

The beach curves away like a boomerang, comes back to what we know.
Among trinkets on the sand a shell lipped in seawater
holding up a mirror. Footprints crisscross with the road not taken,
whole advancements swept aside by the creeping blue.
Who can tell who's been where if we ghost through life humming
to knackered skies? A lifejacket's made of air, only works
if we sink beyond ourselves. Silence carries beyond all knowledge.

Kevin Graham

STINGING FLY PATRONS

Many thanks to:

Hanora Bagnell
Valerie Bistany
Trish Byrne
Brian Cliff
Edmond Condon
Evelyn Conlon
Simon Costello
Sheila Crowley
Paul Curley
Kris Deffenbacher
Andrew Donovan
Gerry Dukes
Ciara Ferguson
Stephen Grant
Brendan Hackett
James Hanley
Sean Hanrahan
Christine Dwyer Hickey
Dennis Houlihan
Nuala Jackson
Geoffrey Keating
Jack Keenan
Jerry Kelleher
Jack Kelleher
Claire Keogh
Joe Lawlor
Irene Rose Ledger
Lucy Luck
Róisín McDermott
Petra McDonough
Lynn McGrane
Jon McGregor
John McInerney

Maureen McLaughlin
Niall MacMonagle
Finbar McLoughlin
Maggie McLoughlin
Ama, Grace & Fraoch MacSweeney
Mary MacSweeney
Paddy & Moira MacSweeney
Anil Malhotra
Gerry Marmion
Ivan Mulcahy
Michael O'Connor
Patrick O'Donoghue
Kieran O'Shea
Lucy Perrem
Maria Pierce
Peter J. Pitkin
George Preble
Orna Ross
Fiona Ruff
Alf Scott
Ann Seery
Attique Shafiq
Eileen Sheridan
Alfie & Savannah Stephenson
Marie Claire Sweeney
Olive Towey
Debbi Voisey
Therese Walsh
Ruth Webster
The Blue Nib (Poetry Website)
Museum of Literature Ireland
Solas Nua

We'd also like to thank those individuals who have expressed the preference to remain anonymous.

By making an annual contribution of 75 euro, patrons provide us with vital support and encouragement.

BECOME A PATRON ONLINE AT STINGINGFLY.ORG

or send a cheque or postal order to:
The Stinging Fly, PO Box 6016, Dublin 1.

Rehan Ali was born in the city of Rawalpindi, Pakistan. At the age of six, his mother fled the country, taking him and his siblings to the land they would come to know as Ireland. He spent his childhood in a hostel named Bridgewater House in Carrick-on-Suir, County Tipperary.

Graham Allen is Professor in English at UCC. His collections, *The One That Got Away* (2014) and *The Madhouse System* (2016), along with his epoem, *Holes*, are published by New Binary Press. A new collection, *No Rainbows Here*, will be published by Salmon in 2020.

Anonymous – the author of 'I had to keep on' is originally from Afghanistan, but does not want to detail the particulars of their identity or current location.

Paddy Bushe was born in Dublin and now lives in Kerry. He is a poet, editor and translator in both Irish and English. Two new books, *Peripheral Vision*, a collection in English, and *Second Sight*, a selection of his poems in Irish with his own translations, will be published by Dedalus Press in 2020.

Mairéad Byrne's current publications include two chapbooks, *In & Out* (Smithereens Press, 2019) and *har sawlya* (above / ground, 2019); work in *The Cast-Iron Airplane That Can Actually Fly: Contemporary Poets Comment on Their Prose Poems* (MadHat, 2019); and an essay, 'Light in July', in *ReRites: Human and A.I. Poetry* (Anteism, 2019).

Jan Carson is a writer and community arts facilitator based in East Belfast. Her books include a novel, *Malcolm Orange Disappears*, a short-story collection, *Children's Children*, and a micro-fiction collection, *Postcard Stories*. Her second novel, *The Fire Starters*, was published by Doubleday in 2019. It won the EU Prize for Literature for Ireland 2019.

Aoife Casby lives on the west coast of Ireland where she swims and grows potatoes. She works as a writer, editor and visual artist. Her short fiction is widely published in literary magazines and journals. She is currently finishing a novel and a PhD.

Heather Christle is the author of four poetry collections. Her first work of nonfiction, *The Crying Book*, will be out in the US in November 2019 and in the UK in February 2020. She teaches creative writing at Emory University in Atlanta.

Sarah Edwards is a writer and editor in Durham, North Carolina. Her poetry and fiction have appeared in *Subtropics*, *The Southern Humanities Review*, *Joyland*, *Ninth Letter*, *The Sycamore Review*, *TYPO*, *Prelude*, and *The Hampden-Sydney Poetry Review*, among others.

Mariana Enriquez is the author of three novels, two collections of short stories and two works of non-fiction in Spanish. Her work has been translated into over twenty languages, and her most recent story collection, *Things We Lost In The Fire*, was published by Granta Books in 2017. Her stories have also appeared in *The New Yorker*, *Granta*, *McSweeney's* and *Asymptote*.

Arnold Thomas Fanning's work has been published in *The Dublin Review*, *Banshee*, *gorse*, *The Lonely Crowd* and elsewhere. It has also been broadcast on RTÉ Radio 1 and BBC Radio 4. *Mind on Fire: A Memoir of Madness and Recovery* was published by Penguin Ireland in 2018 and was shortlisted for the Wellcome Book Prize 2019.

Jessica Foley is a writer, transdisciplinary researcher and teacher based in Dublin. She is currently an IRC postdoctoral fellow at MUSSI (Maynooth University) and writer-at-large with the Orthogonal Methods Group at CONNECT (TCD).

Mia Gallagher's books are *HellFire* (Penguin, 2006), winner of the Irish Tatler Literature Award, *Beautiful Pictures of the Lost Homeland* (New Island, 2016), and *Shift* (New Island, 2018), longlisted for the Edge Hill Short Story Award. Mia is a contributing editor with *The Stinging Fly* and a member of Aosdána.

Kevin Graham's poems have appeared most recently in *Poetry Ireland Review* and in *Causeway*. Smithereens Press published a chapbook, *Traces*, in 2016.

Eamon Grennan, a Dubliner, taught for many years at Vassar College. His collections include *Out of Sight: New & Selected Poems* (Graywolf, 2010), and *There Now* (Gallery Press/Graywolf, 2016). In the past ten years he has been writing and directing 'plays for voices' for Curlew Theatre Company, Connemara.

Eloise Hendy is a writer and poet living in London. She's currently working on a PhD at the University of Sussex on autotheory and the contemporary. Her writing has appeared in *Frieze*, *Ambit*, *The Tangerine*, and *Pain*, among others, and she was shortlisted for The White Review Poet's Prize 2018.

Molly Hennigan is from County Kildare. She is currently based in Massachusetts where she is completing her PhD in English. This essay is one of a series she is working on exploring mental illness and maternal lineage.

Hugo Kelly has won many prizes for his short fiction and has twice been nominated for a Hennessy New Writing Award. He has been published in several journals and anthologies and his short stories have been broadcast on BBC and RTÉ Radio. He works as a librarian in NUI Galway.

Róisín Kelly was born in west Belfast, raised in Leitrim, and currently lives in Cork. Her publications include *Rapture* (Southword Editions, 2016) and *Mercy* (forthcoming from Bloodaxe Books, March 2020). She won the Fish Poetry Prize in 2017.

Hina Khan completed her MFA from Fatima Jinnah Women University, Pakistan in 2003, with Miniature Painting as Major. Hina's work portrays social issues, immigration and humanitarian crises. She's participated in exhibitions in Dublin, Portlaoise and Mayo, and had a solo show in Ballina Arts Centre in 2018. Her next solo show is in County Laois.

Paul Lewis comes from Cork City and lives in Galway. Other work is to be found in *Channel* and forthcoming in *Gastronomica*.

Joe Lines is the author of *Plot* (The Lifeboat, 2018). His poems have also appeared in *Ambit*, *Poetry Ireland Review* and *The Tangerine*. He received awards from the Arts Council of Northern Ireland in 2016 and 2018.

Dr Conor McCabe is a research associate with UCD Equality Studies Centre. He has written extensively on Irish finance and is involved in activist education. He is the author of *Sins of the Father: the Decisions that Shaped the Irish Economy* (2013) and *Money (Sireacht): Longings for Another Ireland* (2018).

Niamh MacCabe was born in Dublin, grew up in Paris, in north-west Ireland, and in Washington DC, where she graduated from the Corcoran School of Art. An award-winning writer, she has been published in Ireland, the UK, and the US. She lives in Leitrim and is currently completing a BA in Writing & Literature.

Aodán McCardle is co-editor at Veer Books. His current practice includes improvised performance, writing and drawing. He has two books, *Shuddered* and *IS ing* (Veer Books) and an online chapbook, *LllOoVvee* (Smithereens Press).

Megan McDowell's translations include works by Alejandro Zambra, Samanta Schweblin, Lina Meruane, Diego Zuñiga, and Alejandro Jodorowsky, and have been featured in *The New Yorker*, *The Paris Review*, *Tin House*, *McSweeney's*, *Granta*, and the *Atlantic Quarterly*, among others. She lives in Santiago, Chile.

Danielle McLaughlin's short story collection, *Dinosaurs on Other Planets*, was published in 2015 by The Stinging Fly Press. In 2019 she won the Sunday Times Audible Short Story Award and was a recipient of a Windham Campbell Prize. A novel, *Retrospective*, is forthcoming in Spring 2021.

Mimmie Malaba is a 20-year-old spoken word poet. Biggest performances include the National Concert Hall in 2019 as part of This Land, a collaboration with singers, musicians, rappers, poets and performers recently arrived in Ireland, and at Electric Picnic in 2018 as part of KaleidSlam. She is currently studying Pre-Nursing.

Chetna Maroo's work has been published in the Bristol and Bridport Prize anthologies and *The Cincinnati Review*.

Alan Jude Moore is from Dublin. His most recent collection was *Zinger* (2013) from Salmon Poetry.

Manuela Moser's poems have appeared in *Poetry Ireland Review*, *Hotel*, *The Tangerine*, and *Copper Nickel*. She runs The Lifeboat poetry press and reading series.

Doireann Ní Ghríofa writes both prose and poetry, in both Irish and English. Among her awards are the Rooney Prize for Irish Literature, a Seamus Heaney Fellowship, and the Ostana Prize (Italy). Her latest book is a bilingual selection of poetry titled *Lies*.

Muireann O'Dwyer teaches politics at the University of Warwick. Her book, *Gender and Race in European Economic Governance*, will be published by Agenda in 2020.

Leeanne Quinn's debut collection of poetry, *Before You*, was published in 2012 by Dedalus Press, and was highly commended in the Forward Prize for Poetry 2013. She was the recipient of an Arts Council Bursary Award in 2012 and 2018. Her second collection is forthcoming with Dedalus Press in 2020.

Elske Rahill is a novelist and short story writer. She was born in Dublin and currently lives in Burgundy with her partner and four children. Her most recent novel, *An Unravelling*, was published by Head of Zeus earlier this year.

Keith Ridgway is a Dubliner and Londoner. He is the author of the novels *Hawthorn & Child*, *Animals*, and other fiction.

Olivia Rosenthall is a bookseller from Essex. 'Food Shop' is her first story to be published.

Evgeny Shtorn is a writer and LGBT researcher. Forced to leave Russia and claim asylum in 2018, he now campaigns actively against direct provision. He works in Create and also co-ordinates a project at the The National Gallery of Ireland. Evgeny deeply appreciates the mentoring support provided by Annemarie Ní Churreáin in writing this text.

Cathy Sweeney's collection of short stories, *Modern Times*, is forthcoming with the Stinging Fly Press in March 2020.

Cathy Thomas lives in London. She holds an MA in creative writing and won an Arvon / Jerwood Mentorship for playwriting. Her stories have been placed in competitions and published in *Banshee*. She is currently working on a short-story collection.

David Toms lives and works in Oslo, Norway. His most recent book is *Northly*, out now from Turas Press.

Jessica Traynor's collections are *Liffey Swim* (2014) and *The Quick* (2018) from Dedalus Press. Forthcoming projects include *Paper Boat*, an opera commissioned by Music for Galway and Galway 2020. She's Carlow Writer in Residence in 2020, and the recipient of the 2020 Banagher Public Art Commission. She is a Creative Fellow at UCD.

Donnah Vuma is originally from Zimbabwe. She lives in direct provision with her three children. She is studying Politics and International Relations with Sociology as a sanctuary scholarship beneficiary at the University of Limerick. She is co-founder of Movement of Asylum Seekers Ireland (MASI) and is founder of a Limerick-based community group, Every Child is Your Child.

Stephen Walsh lives in Dublin. He started writing stories a few years ago. Some of them have been featured in The White Review Short Story Prize and the RTÉ Francis MacManus Short Story Competition. He's currently working on a first collection.

Sharon Whooley is a filmmaker based in Baltimore, County Cork. Her experimental film works have shown at festivals nationally and internationally. With Pat Collins and Eoghan Mac Giolla Bhríde, she was co-writer on *Silence* (2012) and *Song of Granite* (2017). They are currently writing a film based on John Millington Synge's *The Aran Islands*.